Regional Social Studi
Table of Cont

Introduction

Many factors determine who a person will grow to be. The most important factor, usually, is heredity. Other key factors include one's friends and personal experiences, and one's instincts and natural interests. But another influential factor is where that person grows up and lives. A person may endure the chilly winters of the Northeast mountains or the blazing summers of the desert Southwest. Those places certainly impact the person's life and outlook.

We do not, however, live in regional isolation. The modern world has woven a web of interdependency. Each region gives to and takes from the other regions and, indeed, the world. We gain a better sense of where we are today through a knowledge of geography. By giving students geographical information and allowing them to use their own experiences, we can help them to connect the familiar in their lives with the unfamiliar. They can then move more easily from the known features of locale and region to the more unknown quantities of nation and world. Students can begin with the area they know and then expand their knowledge base. Such knowledge will help students in their standardized testing and in their broader academic pursuits.

By showing students their unique qualities because of region and their necessary interaction with other places, we can give them a better perspective of the world in which they live. That broadened perspective is the goal of *Regional Social Studies*.

Organization

This book is broken into three general sections. A regional relations section for the teacher provides basic information about how the states in the region are related. An introductory section for students provides basic material on map skills, the five themes of geography, and a general background of the region under study. The states section for students then gives background information on each individual state. Topics include history, landscape, natural resources, climate, economy, and famous people. A travel guide is included for each state, with details on popular places to visit and activities for students to complete. Each state unit includes map or globe activities, as well as activities on the history, culture, and geography of the state.

Assessment

A variety of assessments is included in *Regional Social Studies*. At the beginning of the book is a general assessment about the region, states in the region, and basic map skills. Assessments are also included in the introductory section for students. Finally, each state unit includes an assessment covering details about that state.

Five Themes of Geography

Regional Social Studies makes use of the five themes of geography: location, place, movement, human/environmental interaction, and regional similarities. Activities are modeled on these themes. Page 15 includes more details on these themes.

Use

This book is meant to supplement the social studies curriculum in the classroom. Map skills help students to improve their sense of location, place, and movement. The regional and state background information serves as reference material for student reports. The travel section helps students to plan real or imaginary trips in their state or region. The low readability level of the information makes it accessible to a wider range of students.

Maps and Globes

Students gain a greater sense of place by knowing their relationship to other places. For this reason, maps and globes are important tools. This book includes several activities that require the use of flat maps, globes, and road maps. Maps of the United States and the world are a handy addition to any classroom.

Regional Background Information

The purpose of *Regional Social Studies* is two-fold: to give students knowledge of geography and map skills; and to broaden their perspective by showing them the interdependencies that exist between states, regions, and the world. It is truly hard for a person to be totally isolated from the modern world. In today's world of advanced technology and global economy, one must understand and develop links between people of different regions of the United States. One can best show these links between states and regions by emphasizing the five themes of geography.

Location

The West Region is the only region in which two of the states are separated from the rest of the United States. That is why the West Region's geography is the most varied and unusual of any of the regions. The states of the West Region share a somewhat common location. They are all in the western part of the United States. The eight Western states in the contiguous United States are roughly located between 33° N and 49° N, and between 102° W and 124° W. Alaska, the most northern of the Western states, is located between 55° N and 71° N, and between 140° W and 168° W. Hawaii, situated in the Pacific Ocean just below the Tropic of Cancer, is between 20° N and 38° N, and between 153° W and 163° W.

As can be seen, the contiguous states in the West Region are somewhat unified by physical location, though Alaska and Hawaii obviously do not fit in this unity. Five of the West Region states have Pacific coastline: California, Oregon, Washington, Alaska, and Hawaii. All of these have some sea-based economy. Alaska, for example, harvests more fish than any other state. The rest of the states are inland, lacking coastline. In fact, some of the inland states have desert areas.

Most of the West states do have a geological similarity. They are all fairly young geologically. Most of the states have young mountains that are still growing. Some of these mountains were first formed by volcanic action, others by movements inside the Earth as the tectonic plates collided. Many of the states are also in proximity of the Pacific Rim of Fire. These

states are still likely to experience some sort of volcanic or earthquake activity. California was hit fairly recently by a severe earthquake that did considerable damage in the San Francisco area. The most severe earthquake in North America struck Alaska in 1964. Some parts of Anchorage sank 30 feet. In addition, a huge tidal wave spawned by the quake flooded coastal areas of Alaska.

Several of the states still have active volcanoes, and most have the remnants of dead volcanoes. Idaho's Craters of the Moon National Monument is an example of this latter group. Alaska still has active volcanoes on the Alaska Peninsula and extending out into the Aleutian Islands. Hawaii also has active volcanoes. And as recently as 1980, Washington was the victim of a serious volcanic explosion. Mount St. Helens erupted in May of that year, destroying everything within eight miles and knocking down trees within 19 miles.

Even with these similarities, the landscape varies greatly in the West. The area contains mountains, glaciers, canyons, and deserts. There are fertile valleys in the mountains, as well as large basin areas between the various mountain ranges.

For every kind of landscape, there is a different kind of climate. Warm Pacific breezes give Hawaii a humid, warm climate. The upper West Coast states have a rainy, cool climate. California often has sunshine, and Alaska often has severe cold. The mountain peaks have constant ice, and the desert areas are hot and dry. As a result, growing seasons vary widely. At Barrow, in far north Alaska, the growing season is about 17 days. In southern California, crops can be grown almost year-round.

Place

Most of the states in the West Region were settled as a result of the Westward Movement. As the young nation expanded, people sought wide, open spaces in which to settle and start farms and towns. Of course, in most cases, the settlers were the last ones to arrive in the West. The explorers arrived first, some charting the West Coast as early as the 1500s, though most of the initial wave of exploration began in the

Regional Background Information

mid-1700s. Captain James Cook of Great Britain visited the Hawaiian Islands, as well as the West Coast and parts of the Alaska coastline. Meriwether Lewis and William Clark are perhaps most responsible for opening the West to settlement. In the early 1800s, they were commissioned by President Thomas Jefferson to explore the new Louisiana Purchase and find a land route to the Pacific Ocean. With the help of several American Indian groups, Lewis and Clark were able to reach the mouth of the Columbia River in 1805.

After the explorers came the traders and trappers. This latter group was responsible for blazing the Oregon Trail that later pioneers and settlers used to move into the Oregon Country. The various gold strikes in the region also helped to increase population so that the territories could eventually gain statehood. The California gold strike in 1848 led to a rapid increase in population there. Similar strikes in Colorado in 1858, Idaho in 1860, and Alaska in 1896 allowed for populations in those places to balloon. Ironically, the rapid growth did not always last. By 1863, for example, Idaho had 70,000 settlers. By 1870, though, the gold rush had ended and only 15,000 settlers remained. Most of the states in the region gained statehood in the latter 1800s. Alaska and Hawaii did not become states until 1959.

Movement

As noted earlier, five of the Western states have Pacific Ocean coastline. These, then, have access to shipping and water transportation. However, the Pacific coastline does not provide the great number of good harbors that the Atlantic coastline does. These Western states do enjoy some sea-based economy. The inland states also have rivers that provide movement capabilities. Colorado and Idaho, especially, have notable rivers. Colorado serves as the source of a variety of large rivers, such as the Colorado, Rio Grande, and Arkansas.

The mountain ranges that stripe the Western region serve as a hindrance to movement. In fact, before explorers found gaps and valleys through the mountains, most travel to the West Coast was done by boat. The mountain ranges also serve to divide the region both geologically and climatically. The region experiences markedly different climate patterns on the two sides of the mountain ranges. On the Pacific side, the climate is typically wet and mild. On the opposite side, the climate is typically drier and more varied in temperature range.

Human/Environmental Interaction

As the region becomes more settled, environmental problems have continued to grow. California now is crowded with people, and smog is often a problem in the Los Angeles vicinity. Colorado's eastern slope is overcrowded with people, and the once clean mountain air and streams have been tainted by pollution. Idaho, likewise, is struggling to maintain the quality of its wilderness areas. Logging activities in the Pacific Northwest have led to the destruction of the habitats of a variety of species. The Exxon *Valdez* oil spill in Alaska demonstrated just how fragile the environment could be and how destructive human carelessness or negligence can be. Most of the states in the region now are struggling with the thorny problem of how to balance growth and progress with the need to preserve the beauty of nature.

People in the West earn a living in a variety of ways. Farming is still an important industry, especially in California and Idaho. Logging, mining, and fishing are also important. Many factories in the region send goods across the country and around the world. As in other regions, most people in the West have service jobs. They work in office jobs, in finance and real estate, and in the legal and medical fields. Many people, especially in Alaska, work for the U.S. government. Service people also work in stores, restaurants, and hospitals. They also help the many tourists that visit the region.

Region

All these regional links, though at times splintered, provide people in the West with a sense of identity. This sense of identity allows students to understand better just who they are. Then they will be able to understand others better, too.

Assessment: West Region

Circle the letter of the correct answer.

1. Alaska is the _____ state in the United States.
   a. smallest
   b. hottest
   c. driest
   d. largest

2. The _____ first claimed the land of California.
   a. Spanish
   b. Russian
   c. British
   d. French

3. The _____ are a major landform in Colorado.
   a. Great Lakes
   b. Coastal Plains
   c. Rocky Mountains
   d. Niagara Falls

4. The Japanese attacked the navy base at _____ in Hawaii in 1941.
   a. Gold Bay
   b. Pearl Harbor
   c. Diamond Mountain
   d. Silver River

5. In 1896, Idaho women won the right to _____.
   a. work
   b. complain
   c. vote
   d. ride horses

6. The Comstock Lode in Nevada was a famous _____.
   a. gold mine
   b. club
   c. silver mine
   d. freight company

7. Many settlers reached Oregon by traveling along the _____.
   a. Wilderness Road
   b. Trail of Tears
   c. Pony Express
   d. Oregon Trail

8. Butch Cassidy _____ in the canyons of Utah.
   a. taught school
   b. hid from law officers
   c. sang to tourists
   d. played football

9. In 1980, a volcano named _____ erupted in Washington.
   a. Mount Olympus
   b. Mount Rainier
   c. Mount Cascade
   d. Mount St. Helens

10. _____ in Wyoming was the first land to be made into a national park.
    a. Yellowstone
    b. Rocky Mountains
    c. Grand Tetons
    d. Black Canyon

Name _____   Date _____

Study the map. Then answer the questions that follow.

11. Which three West states shown have coastline on the Pacific Ocean?

_____

_____

_____

12. The two states west of Idaho are

_____

and _____.

13. The state east of Utah is _____.

14. The state north of Colorado is _____.

15. The state just south of Washington is _____.

Name _____ Date _____

Map Skills

A map is a drawing of a real place. All maps have a title to tell what the map shows. Symbols on the map stand for real things. To know what the symbols stand for, you will need to read the map key, or legend. Most maps also have a compass rose. The compass rose helps you find directions. It tells which direction is north (N), east (E), south (S), or west (W). These directions are called *cardinal directions*.

United States Map

Answer the questions.

1. What is the title of the map? _____

2. What does the compass rose tell you? _____

3. What does the star symbol in the legend mean? _____

4. Which state is east of Indiana? _____

5. Which country borders the United States to the south? _____

6. Which state touches land only on its northern border? _____

Name _____   Date _____

Map Skills

Reading a Road Map

There are many kinds of maps. People are most familiar with road maps. These maps show roads, distances, rest areas, parks, and places of interest.

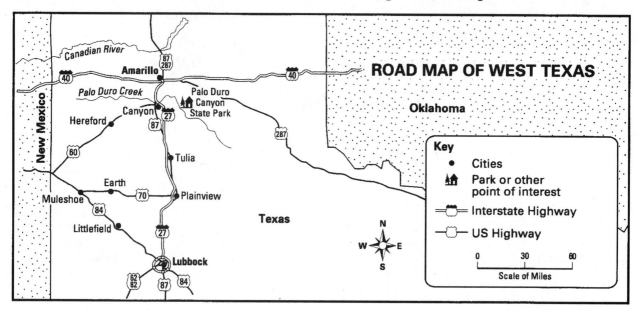

Answer the questions.

1. Find Amarillo on the map. What is the major east-west road that passes through Amarillo?

_____

2. Find Lubbock on the map. What is the distance between Amarillo and Lubbock?

_____

3. Find Muleshoe on the map. What direction(s) would you travel from Amarillo to Muleshoe?

_____

4. What is the name of the park near Amarillo?

_____

Name _____ Date _____

Map Skills

Reading a Resource Map

Some maps show only one kind of information. A *population* map shows how many people live in different areas. A *precipitation* map shows how much rain or rain and snow an area gets each year. The map below is a *resource* map. This map shows where different kinds of trees and forests grow in the United States.

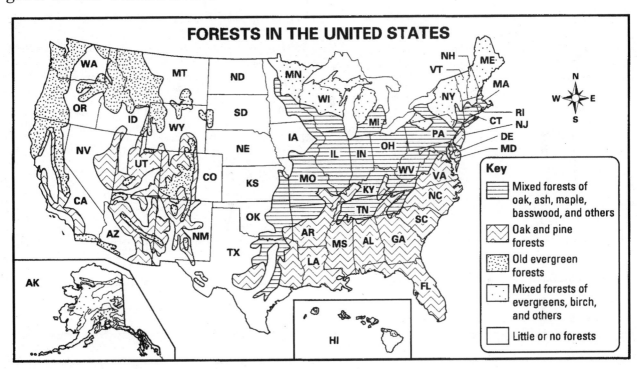

FORESTS IN THE UNITED STATES

Key
- Mixed forests of oak, ash, maple, basswood, and others
- Oak and pine forests
- Old evergreen forests
- Mixed forests of evergreens, birch, and others
- Little or no forests

Answer the questions.

1. In which state would you find old evergreen forests?

_____

2. What kind of forest grows in the Northwest part of the United States?

_____

3. How many kinds of trees or forests are in Colorado? Name them.

_____

4. Find the state where you live. What kinds of trees or forests grow in your state?

_____

Map Assessment

Look at the map. Then answer the questions.

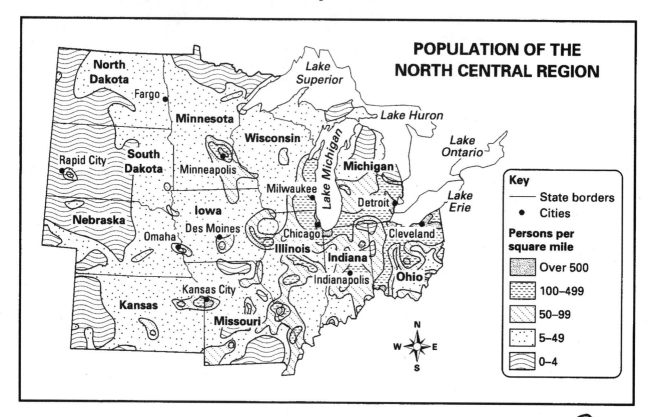

POPULATION OF THE NORTH CENTRAL REGION

Key
— State borders
• Cities
Persons per square mile
Over 500
100–499
50–99
5–49
0–4

1. What is the name of this map?

_____

2. What symbol is used to show cities?

_____

3. Which state is south of Minnesota?

_____

4. About how many people per square mile live in Fargo, North Dakota?

_____

The West

The states along the Pacific Ocean and those that extend to the Rocky Mountains are in the western part of the United States. The area has deserts, beaches, canyons, and mountains. Spain, Russia, and Great Britain have been part of the development of this area. However, a young United States had the greatest effect on the making of the West.

History

The first people to live in the West were Native Americans. There were many different groups because the land varied greatly. Some groups lived in forests and hunted. Others lived in deserts and gathered food from plants. Others, still, lived along beaches. They fished. Spain was the first group to explore the West closely. Spanish explorers came up from Mexico looking for gold. The English discovered Hawaii. Russians traveled into Alaska. The Appalachian Mountains and the Rocky Mountains had blocked the way for people in the eastern part of the United States. Once a path was found over the mountains in the 1830s, the pioneers poured into the West.

The first movement west came with trappers who were looking for furs to trade. They were often friends with the Native Americans. Soon, people began to move west to find cheap land. They wanted to start ranches and farms. When gold was found in California, huge groups of people headed to California. The gold rush was on. Some traveled by sea in ships. Most traveled by wagons over the mountains. Other states began to find gold, too. As late as 1896, Alaska started its first gold rush.

The natives had few diseases. When they came in contact with the travelers, many became sick. In some cases, whole villages of natives died from diseases. Also, the Native Americans became angry at the loss of their land and the number of people who traveled across it. Some attacked the wagons and settlers. The United States government passed laws to send the Native Americans to reservations. Reservations were areas of land. The reservations were often located in places far from their homes.

By the end of the 1800s, the West and East were connected by telegraph wires and train tracks. The gold rush had ended in most states, but other important minerals, such as petroleum and natural gas, had been found. Mining these materials was a main source of jobs for people.

The West

Ranching and farming were also important. Even today, the economy of most of the western states is still tied to the land.

Landscape

The land varies greatly in the West. There is everything from mountains to glaciers to deserts. The mountains are young. Some were made by volcanoes, others by movement of land inside the Earth. There are deep valleys in the mountains, as well as flat areas called basins. Some states have desert areas, while others have flat, grassy plains. On these plains, a mesa may rise up. A mesa is a mountain with steep sides and a flat top. Deep canyons cover miles of land. Bits of sand are washed away by rain or blown away by wind. As a result, huge stone towers stand like statues. Finally, there are icy glaciers that cover the land in Alaska.

Climate

For every kind of landscape, there is a different kind of climate. Warm Pacific Ocean breezes give Hawaii a humid, wet climate. Other states on the coast get a rainy, cool climate. Here, the seasons change little. Farmers may be able to grow crops all year. Those states near mountains may be freezing in the winters, but rainy and cool in the summer. Deserts are hot and dry. Some states with deserts receive less than 16 inches of rain each year. In the winter, the plains may get as cold as in the mountains.

Natural Resources

The find of gold caused a huge change in the growth of the United States. Once the gold ran out, people began to find other minerals in large amounts. Petroleum, copper, silver, and natural gas are among those most common in the western states. The beauty of the land itself is as much a resource as the minerals. Some states have unusual parts of nature that cannot be found anywhere else in the United States. For example, Yellowstone National Park has geysers, California has redwood trees over 300 feet tall, and Hawaii has unusual trees, flowers, and animals. The state governments quickly recognized the land as a resource. Much land is part of parks for safekeeping. The one resource many western states lack is water.

Economy

People in the West earn a living in many ways. Mining is still an

The West

important job. Minerals include petroleum, copper, and natural gas. Raising cattle and sheep is also a source of income for many people. Fishing in the Pacific Ocean provides much seafood. However, most people in the West work in service jobs. Service people help other people. Service people work in stores, restaurants, and hospitals. The beauty of the land and cities that focus on entertainment attract tourists. Service people also help the people who visit the region.

Higher Education

Education has always been important to the settlers that moved west. They wanted their children to do well in the world. Some settlements started schools in a person's home. Eventually these schools became universities. California has the largest group of colleges and universities in the United States. California State University leads the group. There are 20 campuses that work together as the California State University. Utah has several colleges, the largest being the University of Utah. Utah is proud of the fact that more of its students graduate from high school than any other state.

The West Today

The states in the West were built on dreams and on hard work. Many settlers started with nothing. In the case of the Native Americans, the natives were forced off the land and into places they did not choose. Their lives were destroyed. As the West faces the new century, there are several problems people there will need to deal with. First is the recognition of the native traditions and stories. Many native groups are teaching the next generation the language of their ancestors. They are also teaching them the history of their people.

Second, the West has a very short supply of water. The lack of rivers and rain means that the states will need to find ways to provide water. Some states already have some ways to recycle snow and other water.

Finally, the beauty of the land is very valuable. As more people and businesses move to the West, land is cleared and developed. Most of nature's treasures are already protected in state and national parks. However, more people mean pollution and trash. History proves that the people in the western states are ready for the challenge.

The West Assessment

Circle the letter of the correct answer.

1. _____ had the greatest effect on the development of the West.
   a. Mexico
   b. Soviet Republic
   c. United States
   d. Great Britain

2. The _____ borders the west coast of the United States.
   a. Atlantic Ocean
   b. Pacific Ocean
   c. Rocky Mountains
   d. Colorado River

3. People could not move west because _____.
   a. two sets of mountains blocked the path
   b. there were no roads
   c. it was too hot
   d. it was against the law

4. Many people moved west to find _____.
   a. gold
   b. cattle
   c. Native Americans
   d. dreams

5. Reservations are _____.
   a. large farms
   b. the Native American's hunting land
   c. places where Native Americans were forced to live
   d. cattle ranches

6. The water supply is low in the Western area because many states _____.
   a. use it all in factories
   b. get little rain or snow
   c. do not have rivers
   d. drink it

7. Yellowstone National Park has _____ that are not found in any other place in the United States.
   a. gold
   b. snow
   c. tall trees
   d. geysers

8. Most people in the Western states work in _____.
   a. mining
   b. colleges
   c. service jobs
   d. ranching

9. Utah has the highest number of people who _____.
   a. graduate from high school
   b. play a guitar
   c. go fishing
   d. raise cattle

10. Many Native Americans are _____.
    a. moving off the reservations
    b. teaching their children about their history
    c. opening restaurants
    d. happy on the reservations

Name _____ Date _____

The Five Themes of Geography

Where people live affects every part of their life, from the foods they eat to the jobs they can do. The Five Themes of Geography help us to look at the importance of a place in our lives.

LOCATION Where is it?

Location tells exactly where a place is located. It can include latitude and longitude, cardinal directions, or even just the words "next to."

PLACE What does it look like?

Place is the part of an area you see. It includes landforms, rivers, or buildings in a city.

MOVEMENT How do people, goods, and ideas move from one place to another?

Movement looks at how and why things move. It looks at why people leave a country, how goods are moved, and how both affect the land or people.

INTERACTION How do people use or change the land?

Interaction is how people use or change the environment, the area in which they live. It looks at where people have parks, build cities, or farm.

REGION How are different places in an area alike?

Region looks at the way an area is divided. A region has characteristics that are the same. Often areas are grouped because the people share a language, people do the same kind of work, or the landforms are the same.

Name _____ Date _____

United States Map

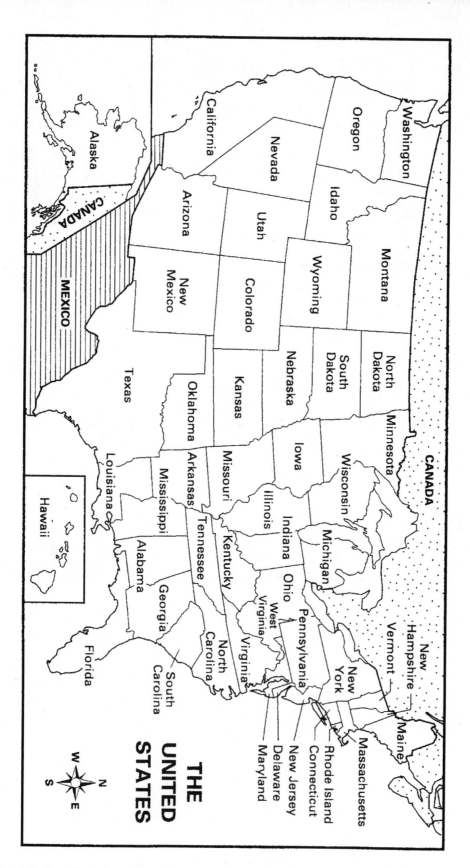

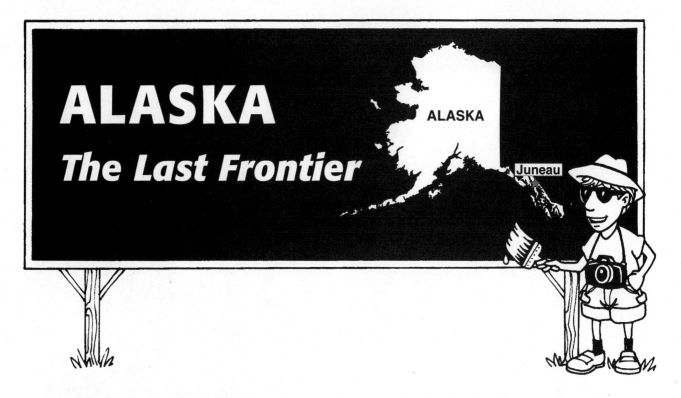

State Your Facts!

Capital: Juneau

Abbreviation: AK

Statehood: January 3, 1959—the 49th state

Motto: "North to the Future"

Bird: Willow ptarmigan

Flower: Forget-me-not

Tree: Sitka spruce

Area: 589,878 sq mi
(1,522,596 sq km)—1st in size

Five largest cities: Anchorage, Fairbanks, Juneau, College, Sitka

Highest point: Mount McKinley—20,320 ft
(6,194 m)

Name _____   Date _____

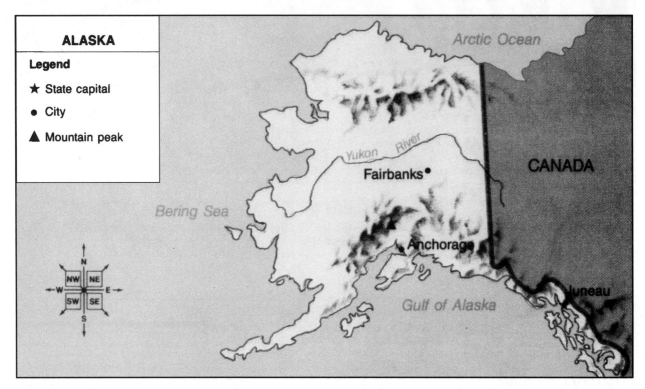

A relief map is used to show the topography, or landscape, of a place. Relief maps show the high and low features of the land.

Study the map on this page. Read the legend. What does each symbol stand for? Find the compass rose. What is it used for? Now complete the exercises below.

1. Follow the directions below to finish the map.
   a. Write <u>Brooks</u> <u>Range</u> on the mountain range in northern Alaska.
   b. Write <u>Alaska</u> <u>Range</u> on the southern mountain range near Anchorage.
   c. Write <u>Coast</u> <u>Range</u> along the southern mountain range near Juneau.
   d. Write <u>Mount</u> <u>McKinley</u> near the mountain peak between Anchorage and Fairbanks.

2. What river flows between the Brooks Range and the Alaska Range?

   _____

3. Does the Yukon River run through a valley or a mountain range?

   _____

ALASKA – *The Last Frontier*

Ask About Alaska!

Alaska is the largest state in the nation. It is also the most northern. Even more important, Alaska is America's last frontier. The name of the state is an Aleut word meaning "great land." It is truly that.

History

About 15,000 years ago, Alaska and Siberia in Asia were probably connected by an ice bridge. Ancient people migrated across the bridge. Then the ice melted. Now the Bering Strait separates the two landmasses.

Some of the early American Indian groups in Alaska were the Inuit and the Aleuts. The Inuit lived in the north and west parts of the area. They hunted whales, walrus, and seals in the ocean. They also hunted bear and caribou. The Aleuts lived on a string of islands. These islands extend southwest from the Alaska mainland. They are called the Aleutian Islands. The Aleuts also depended on the ocean for survival. Many members of these groups still live in Alaska today.

Alaska attracted few explorers until the 1700s. Then Czar Peter I of Russia wanted to know if his country was attached to North America. He sent a Danish sea

captain, Vitus Bering, to find out. In 1728, Bering sailed north and passed through the Bering Strait. He learned the two continents were no longer connected.

In 1784, the Russians built the first permanent settlement in Alaska. It was on Kodiak Island. Later, in 1799, Czar Paul I claimed all of Alaska for Russia. The area became known as Russian America. In 1867, Russia sold Alaska to the United States for $7.2 million.

In 1896, gold was discovered in the Klondike. Thousands of gold seekers headed north to Alaska. Alaska's population grew rapidly. Other places had gold rushes, too.

In 1900, Juneau was made the capital of Alaska. The area became a U.S. territory in 1912. In World War II, Japan captured two islands in the Aleutians. A supply road was built north to Alaska from the U. S.. It was called the Alaska Highway. It is still used today.

As the 20th century continued, Alaska's economy grew slowly. Fishing became very important in Alaska. Canning and timber

Ask About Alaska!

processing also became important industries. In 1957, oil was discovered in Alaska. Finally, in 1959, Alaska became the 49th member of the United States.

Since then, the state has had its ups and downs. In 1964, a severe earthquake hit south-central Alaska. Parts of Anchorage sank 30 feet. A huge tidal wave caused by the quake destroyed coastal areas.

Then more oil and natural gas were discovered in northeast Alaska. The Alaska Pipeline was built to move the oil. It was completed in 1977. But then a disaster occurred. A ship full of oil, the Exxon *Valdez*, wrecked. It spilled millions of gallons of oil. Many animals died or had their homes destroyed.

Now Alaska tries to balance its need for growth with its need to protect nature. The next century will tell how well the state has done.

Landscape

Alaska is the largest state in the U.S. It measures about 1,350 miles (2,150 km) from north to south. It is about 2,350 miles (3,800 km) at its widest. It also has about 6,640 miles (10,686 km) of coastline.

Alaska has many mountains. One group of mountains, the Pacific System, runs parallel to the coastline. The highest peak in North America, Mount McKinley, is in this system. Mount McKinley is in south-central Alaska. There are also glaciers and volcanoes in this system. Good farmland and most of Alaska's cities are found in this system, too.

North and west of this system is the Central Plateau. It is broad and low, with a few mountains. Fairbanks is on this plateau. North of the plateau is the Arctic System of mountains. North of the Arctic System, the Arctic Slope dips to the Arctic Ocean. During most of the year, it is a frozen wasteland. There are also active volcanoes in Alaska. Some are on the Alaska Peninsula. Others are in the Aleutian Islands.

Climate

Alaska has several climates. All of them could be described as cool or cold. Southeast Alaska has the mildest weather. It is protected from cold north winds by mountains. It also gets warming winds from the Pacific Ocean. Temperatures there range from -15° F to a rare 90° F.

The interior of Alaska has extremes of weather. There it can

ALASKA – *The Last Frontier*

be -75° F or up to 100° F. The north part of Alaska is usually cold. The summers are cool, and the winters are long and cold.

At Barrow, in far north Alaska, the growing season is about 17 days. Fairbanks, on the Central Plateau, has a growing season of about 89 days. Juneau, on the southeast coast, has a growing season of about 172 days.

Natural Resources

Alaska is rich in natural resources. The oceans provide much seafood. The many forests supply timber for lumber and wood products. Gold, sand, and gravel are mined in the state. So are silver, copper, zinc, and lead. Alaska also has huge deposits of oil and natural gas.

Economy

Mining is an important source of wealth in Alaska. So is fishing. Alaska harvests more fish than any other state. Agriculture is only a small part of the economy.

Service jobs are important, too. The state's biggest employer is the federal government. Many military bases are located in the state. Many other service workers help tourists that visit the state.

Many native Alaskans still make money by trapping animals for fur. They also make traditional art. Their works include beadwork, totem poles, carved ivory, and tribal clothing.

Higher Education

The University of Alaska was founded in 1917. Its main campus is in College. The state also has a system of community colleges.

Famous People

Jay Hammond was governor of Alaska from 1974 to 1982. His main goal was to preserve Alaska's natural beauty. Before he became governor, he was a bush pilot.

Alaska Today

Alaska is America's "last frontier." It is a vast land of ice and snow, forests, and mountains. The people of Alaska want growth and progress for their 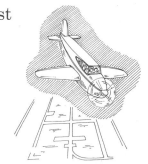 state. But they also want to hold on to Alaska's natural beauty. Alaskans must work hard to keep the delicate balance.

Assessment

Circle the letter of the correct answer.

1. When Alaska was claimed by Russia, it was called _____.
   a. Russian America   b. Siberia
   c. Beringville   d. Fairbanks

2. Alaska is the _____ state in the United States.
   a. smallest   b. hottest
   c. driest   d. largest

3. There are many active _____ in the Aleutian Islands.
   a. earthquakes   b. volcanoes
   c. reindeer farms   d. gold mines

Number the events in the order they happened.

_____ Alaska became the 49th state.

_____ Russia sold Alaska to the United States.

_____ The Exxon *Valdez* wrecked and
        spilled oil.

_____ Vitus Bering explored the Alaska
        area in 1728.

_____ The first permanent European settlement in
        Alaska was started on Kodiak Island.

_____ Gold was discovered in the Klondike.

_____ A severe earthquake struck south-central Alaska.

Travel Time!

Before you plan your Alaskan vacation, there are a few things you should remember. Alaska is huge. Many places there are remote. There are no roads to many places. Some places can only be reached by boat or plane. That's why good bush pilots are in demand in the state. They fly people to remote spots on the Alaskan frontier.

Do you like cold weather and wilderness? Then Alaska has places for you to go. The state has several national parks. Katmai National Park has mountains, glaciers, and volcanoes. It is a great place to fish. This park, in southwest Alaska, is best reached by boat or plane. Denali National Park features Mount McKinley. This is the tallest mountain in North America. This park is in south-central Alaska.

Northern Alaska has the Kobuk Valley National Park. Also in the north part of the state is Gates of the Arctic National Park. Southwest Alaska has Lake Clark National Park and Katmai National Park.

Glacier Bay National Park is in southeast Alaska. This park has 16 glaciers. It is a good place to see whales and seals. You can also see mountain goats and brown bears there.

A special treat is to cross Alaska on the Alaska Railroad. It provides freight and passenger services. It travels along the coast from Seward and Whittier to Anchorage. Then it heads inland to Fairbanks. The train passes through 400 miles of wilderness forests. Sometimes it stops for moose or caribou on the tracks. Other times it stops to pick up people by the track. You only have to wave, and the engineer will stop to pick you up.

A famous event in Alaska is the Iditarod Trail Sled Dog Race. It is held each March. The race begins in Anchorage. Then the racers drive the dogsleds 1,150 miles (1,840 km) to the northwest. The race ends in Nome, on the west coast of Alaska. Most racers, who are called mushers, finish the race in about 13 days.

Travel Time!

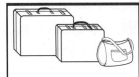

Pack Your Bags!

- Pretend that you are going to race in the Iditarod Trail Sled Dog Race. Most mushers keep traveling much of the day and night. What do you think you would need to take on the trip? Make a list of supplies. What would you do each day? Write a story about one day in the race. Draw a picture of you with your dogsled.

On the Road!

- Imagine that you are a bush pilot. What do you think you would see as you fly across the wilds of Alaska? Write a short description. Include a picture to go with your description.
- Pretend that you are crossing Alaska on the Alaska Railroad. Write a journal entry that tells what you see on one day of travel. Include a picture to go with your journal entry.

Snapshots!

- Kodiak bears are large brown bears that live in Alaska. Write a short story or poem about meeting a Kodiak bear in the forest. Include a picture with your writing.
- Draw a picture of a totem pole. Include animal heads as part of the pole. Color your finished drawing with bright colors.
- Pretend that you live in far north Alaska. It is sometimes called the "land of the midnight Sun." Sometimes the Sun shines all the time. Sometimes it is dark or dim all day long. Write a poem about living in this kind of place. Include a picture with your poem.

ALASKA – *The Last Frontier*

CALIFORNIA
The Golden State

══ State Your Facts! ══

Capital: Sacramento

Abbreviation: CA

Statehood: September 9, 1850—the 31st state

Motto: *Eureka* ("I Have Found It")

Bird: California valley quail

Flower: Golden poppy

Tree: California redwood

Area: 158,648 sq mi (410,896 sq km)—3rd in size

Five largest cities: Los Angeles, San Diego, San Jose, San Francisco, Long Beach

Highest point: Mount Whitney—14,494 ft (4,418 m)

Sports teams: San Francisco 49ers (football), Oakland Raiders (football), San Diego Chargers (football), Golden State Warriors (basketball), Los Angeles Clippers (basketball), Los Angeles Lakers (basketball), Sacramento Kings (basketball), Los Angeles Sparks (women's basketball), Sacramento Monarchs (women's basketball), Anaheim Angels (baseball), Oakland Athletics (baseball), Los Angeles Dodgers (baseball), San Diego Padres (baseball), San Francisco Giants (baseball), Anaheim Mighty Ducks (hockey), Los Angeles Kings (hockey), San Jose Sharks (hockey), Los Angeles Galaxy (soccer), San Jose Clash (soccer)

Name _____ Date _____

You can find a place on a map grid by looking it up in the map index. A map index is an alphabetical list of the places on the map. A map index lists each place with the letter and number of its grid.

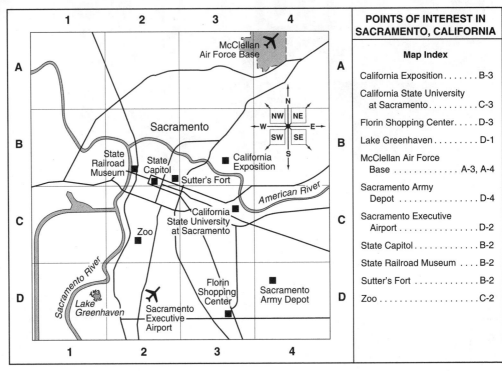

POINTS OF INTEREST IN SACRAMENTO, CALIFORNIA

Map Index

California Exposition B-3

California State University
    at Sacramento C-3

Florin Shopping Center D-3

Lake Greenhaven D-1

McClellan Air Force
    Base A-3, A-4

Sacramento Army
    Depot D-4

Sacramento Executive
    Airport D-2

State Capitol B-2

State Railroad Museum B-2

Sutter's Fort B-2

Zoo C-2

The map shows places of interest in Sacramento, California. To find places on the map, you use the map index. Suppose you want to visit the zoo. Look up *Zoo* in the index. It tells you the zoo is in square C-2. To find this square on the map, put your finger on the C and slide it across row C until you reach column 2. This is square C-2. You can now find the zoo.

Answer the questions below.

1. In which square is Lake Greenhaven? _____

2. In which square is Florin Shopping Center? _____

3. In which square is Sutter's Fort? _____ Name two other points

   of interest located in this square. _____ _____

4. Find McClellan Air Force Base. Now find Sacramento Army Depot.
   Which direction would you travel to get from McClellan Air Force Base

   to the Sacramento Army Depot? _____

Called to California!

Many people have been called to California from the beginning of this state's history. There are a wide variety of resources, and the climate is mild. More people call California home than any other state in the nation. What other reasons make this state so popular?

History

Many Native-American nations lived in peace in the area. Most groups fished and hunted. They collected fruits and vegetables that grew in the wild. The Spanish first visited the land in 1540. They sailed up the Colorado River. They soon explored the California coast. They were looking for gold and a passageway from the Pacific Ocean to the Atlantic Ocean. Even though the Spanish visited, they did not claim the land for Spain. Robert Drake of England claimed it for his country first. The English never settled the land, though.

By the early 1700s, Russian explorers from Alaska began to visit the northern part of California. At the same time, Spanish missionaries began to move into the area from Mexico. The missionaries wanted to teach

Christianity to the natives. They also wanted to keep Russia away from the land. They built missions, small religious settlements, all through the land.

By the 1800s, the Spanish were forced out of Mexico. California became part of this country. Soon, many people came to California. They traveled across the Rocky Mountains from the United States. They came to trap animals for the furs. They also came for the land. People began to buy ranches, some as large as 50,000 acres in size.

The United States wanted to buy California from Mexico. But Mexico would not sell the land. Some people in California wanted to form their own country. The United States was already fighting to win control of Texas in the Mexican War. When the United States won in 1848, Mexico also gave up the land rights to California. California became a territory of the United States.

CALIFORNIA – The Golden State

Called to California!

The year 1848 also marked another big event in the history of California.  James Marshall was building a mill for John Sutter. Marshall found a nugget of gold. News spread quickly. Within one year, nearly 80,000 people traveled to California. Many came to find gold. Others started businesses that sold goods to people with gold. In 1850, California joined the United States.

Growth continued at a fast pace. In the late 1860s, Central Pacific Railroad was built from the Atlantic coast to the Pacific coast to join the two together. Immigrants from China worked to lay the rails. Travel became much faster and easier. People went to California looking for cheap land. They built ranches and farms. Irrigation, watering plants through a man-made system of pipes, helped farmers grow fruit and vegetables.

A huge earthquake hit San Francisco in 1906. Fires broke out throughout the city. As the people began to rebuild, another problem began to brew. The United States and Japan began to argue. The United States did not want more Japanese to come into the country. People began to make laws to stop Asians, Japanese and Chinese, from owning land and having other rights. This was discrimination.

The wealth of the state grew. Because of the mild climate and variety of landscapes, movies were often made in California. Oil was discovered, and manufacturing was becoming important with the invention of new machines. World War II fueled a need for aircraft. California led the way. However, the discrimination of Asians was a problem. Americans who were born to Asian parents were put in camps during World War II. They were forced to leave their homes with only what they could carry.

After the war, many servicemen stayed in California. With all the people, pollution of air and water became a concern for the people. But job opportunities grew, especially with the computer companies. At the same time, California has lived through three more earthquakes. Repair of the damage cost billions of dollars. The state has also faced fires in which

Called to California!

large areas of land were burned. But the people of California continue to rise above their problems and look forward to the future.

Landscape

California has a variety of landscapes. Mountains and valleys dot the state. There is nearly 840 miles (1,352 km) of rugged coastline. The Sonoran Desert lies in the south of the state. Death Valley, just north of the desert area, is the lowest point in the state and the nation. This point is 282 feet (86 m) below sea level.

Climate

Temperatures in California vary with the landscape. However, the climate for most of the state is mild. California has an average temperature of 55° F. There are basically two seasons—wet and dry. Growing seasons can last for 120 days in the mountains. But with the mild climate, farmers can grow produce most of the year in the southern areas of California.

Natural Resources

California is rich in natural resources. It ranks first in forests. Huge trees, called redwoods, tower above the ground. Many are over 300 feet tall. Joined with the lakes and  rivers, California has a wealth of land resources. The soil is also rich in minerals. Minerals that California produces include petroleum and gold. The soil itself is good for farming.

Economy

Because of the mild climate and the many kinds of landscape, tourism is very important to the state. Most of the people in California work in service jobs that help the visitors. They may work in restaurants, parks, or stores. The movie business is also important to California. Other sources of income include farming, such as grapes and oranges, computer products, and airplane companies.

CALIFORNIA – The Golden State

Called to California!

Higher Education

California has the largest group of colleges and universities in the nation. California State University has 20 campuses and is the nation's largest state-funded school system. Other schools include California Institute of the Arts and San Diego State.

Famous People

California has many famous people who either were born in the state or lived there. Cesar Chavez was the son of Mexican migrant farmworkers. The family moved from farm to farm to pick the crops. The people worked long hours for little pay. Chavez formed a worker's union for Mexican-American farmworkers. Richard Nixon was the 37th President, and Ronald Reagan, a former Hollywood actor, was the 40th president. Another Hollywood legend is George Lucas. He helped direct and produce the *Star Wars* movies. Astronaut Sally Ride was born and raised in California. She flew on two *Challenger*

space trips. Finally, John Steinbeck, a prize-winning writer, lived in California. He wrote fictional stories about life in the factories and fields of California.

California Today

The state of California is a leader in many ways. It grows more farm crops than any other state. It leads the nation in tourism. It claims the lowest point in the nation. When disaster strikes in the form of earthquakes, it rebuilds. Immigrants from other countries see California as the land of opportunity. People from Central America, Asia, and Europe flood into the state in large numbers. California is a melting pot. These newcomers bring more variety to the state. However, the number of people brings many challenges. Pollution and traffic are at an all-time high. The state has passed many laws to protect its environment. New schools are being built to teach the children. Just as California successfully rebuilds after each earthquake, the people will face each problem and find ways to make the state successful.

CALIFORNIA – *The Golden State*

Name _____ Date _____

Circle the letter of the correct answer.

1. The nickname of California is _____.
   a. The Golden State
   b. The Earthquake State
   c. The First State
   d. The Gold Rush State

2. The _____ first claimed the land of California.
   a. Spanish
   b. Russian
   c. British
   d. French

3. California became a territory of the United States after the _____.
   a. American Revolution
   b. gold rush
   c. Civil War
   d. Mexican War

4. In 1906, there was a _____ that hit San Francisco.
   a. huge earthquake   b. tornado
   c. tidal wave   d. forest fire

5. California became a popular place to make movies because there was a variety of _____.
   a. food that was grown there
   b. people to work in the pictures
   c. landscapes to make pictures
   d. people with money

6. Ronald Reagan was an actor and _____.
   a. a Native American
   b. a United States President
   c. store owner during the gold rush
   d. *Challenger* astronaut

CALIFORNIA – *The Golden State*

Name _____ Date _____

Travel Time!

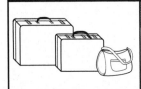

Pack Your Bags!

- Plan a two-week trip in California. Choose the places you will visit and decide how long you will stay in each.

On the Road!

California: Places to Visit and Regional Events

1. State Indian Museum
2. Restored Gold Rush Town
3. Scotty's Castle
4. Hearst Castle
5. Disneyland
6. Marineland
7. San Diego Zoo
8. Chinese New Year Celebration (January)
9. Jumping Frog Jubilee (May)
10. Rodeo (July)
11. Old Spanish Days Fiesta (August)
12. Monterey Jazz Festival (September)

California: Parks and Forests

1. Redwood
2. Lava Beds
3. Lassen Volcanic
4. Muir Woods
5. Yosemite
6. Devils Postpile
7. Sequoia
8. Death Valley
9. Pinnacles
10. Channel Islands
11. Joshua Tree
12. Kings Canyon

Snapshots

- Of all the things you want to visit in California, which would you like to see the most?

COLORADO
The Centennial State

═══ **State Your Facts!** ═══

Capital: Denver

Abbreviation: CO

Statehood: August 1, 1876—the 38th state

Motto: *Nil sine Numine* ("Nothing without Providence")

Bird: Lark bunting

Flower: Rocky Mountain columbine

Tree: Blue spruce

Area: 104,091 sq mi (269,595 sq km)— 8th in size

Five largest cities: Denver, Colorado Springs, Aurora, Lakewood, Pueblo

Highest point: Mount Elbert—14,433 ft (4,399 m)

Sports teams: Colorado Rockies (baseball), Denver Broncos (football), Denver Nuggets (basketball), Colorado Avalanche (hockey), Colorado Rapids (soccer)

Name _____   Date _____

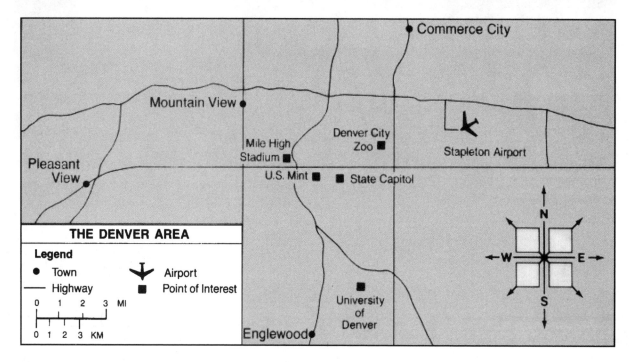

Most maps have a distance scale. This scale allows you to measure how far apart places on the map are. A map scale may use, for example, one inch on the map to equal 20 miles in the real place shown by the map.

Study the map on this page. Read the legend. What does each symbol stand for? Find the compass rose. What is it used for? Find the map scale. The scale goes up to how many miles?

Use the map and the edge of a piece of paper to figure these distances. Write the distance in miles for questions 1 through 4. Write the distance in kilometers for question 5.

1. From Stapleton Airport to Mile High Stadium is about

   _____ miles.

2. From the Denver City Zoo to Englewood is about

   _____ miles.

3. From the State Capitol to the University of Denver is about

   _____ miles.

4. From the U.S. Mint to Commerce City is about

   _____ miles.

5. From Pleasant View to Mountain View is about

   _____ kilometers.

Cruisin' in Colorado!

Do you like the outdoors, mountain peaks, and rugged living? Then you'll like Colorado. That's where you can get a "Rocky Mountain high."

History

 American Indians have lived in the Colorado area for at least 10,000 years. The early people were called the Anasazi, or "ancient ones." Later groups included the Navajo, Hopi, and Zuni. These groups are sometimes called Pueblo Indians. They built multilevel cliff homes.

The Spanish were the first Europeans to explore the area. They came north from Mexico, looking for gold.

In 1803, the U.S. bought a large chunk of land in the West. It was called the Louisiana Purchase. Much of Colorado was included. American explorers began to visit the area. One was Zebulon M. Pike, who arrived in 1806. He gave his name to the famous Pikes Peak. Other trappers and fur traders moved into the area. They were known as "mountain men." In 1833, Bent's Fort was founded. It was the first permanent town in Colorado.

Mexico and the U.S. went to war in 1846. They were fighting for land they both claimed. U.S. troops won every battle. In 1848, the final treaty ending the war was signed. The U.S. gained much land from Mexico. The land covered eight present-day states, including west Colorado.

Gold was discovered in Colorado in 1858. People began to rush to the area to find the yellow metal. By 1859, there were 100,000 settlers in Colorado. But there was a problem. The settlers were on land given to American Indian groups by the U.S. government. But the settlers did not care. They ignored the government. There was no real law and order on the frontier. The people ruled themselves.

Oil was discovered in 1862. Farms and ranches dotted the area. Colorado was becoming settled. In 1876, Colorado became the 38th state. It is called the "Centennial State." It gained statehood 100 years after the *Declaration of Independence* was signed.

Problems with the Indians continued. The government told the Indians to stay in certain places. Many of the Indians refused. Battles broke out. Finally, in the 1880s, the Indian wars ended. The Indian groups were moved to reservations.

COLORADO – *The Centennial State*

Cruisin' in Colorado!

The railroad pushed its way westward. Denver became an important shipping point. Silver, coal, and oil were shipped from the state. Farming also became more important.

In the 1930s, the Great Depression struck Colorado. Banks closed, and businesses failed. People lost their jobs. Worse, a drought in the state lasted from 1932 to 1937. Farmland dried up, and farms failed, too. The area became part of the "Dust Bowl."

Colorado continues to develop. Since the 1950s, dams, reservoirs, and tunnels have been built. These provide water for farming. As in other states, Colorado has problems with air and water pollution. Even with these problems, Colorado has fulfilled its golden promise.

Landscape

Colorado is one of the larger states. It measures 276 miles (444 km) from north to south. It is 387 miles (623 km) wide. The state has three main landforms: plains, mountains, and plateaus. The High Plains section of the Great Plains enters Colorado from the east. It rises gently to the foothills of the mountains. The plains part is mostly level, with some rolling hills. The Rocky Mountains sweep through Colorado in two bands. These high, young mountains cover two fifths of the state. The Colorado Plateau region contains plateaus, canyons, basins, and mesas.

Colorado has several major rivers. The Colorado River begins in northern Colorado. It drains much of western Colorado. The Rio Grande begins in southwest Colorado and flows south to New Mexico and Texas. The Arkansas River starts in the middle of the state and flows eastward into Kansas. The state also has many natural lakes in the mountain areas.

Climate

Colorado is inland, far from major sources of moisture. It has a high elevation. It has several mountain ranges running in different directions. All these make Colorado's climate hard to describe. The state does have low humidity and much sunshine. It also has wide daily and seasonal ranges in temperature. The mountains usually have mild daytime temperatures in the summer. The winters are very cold, with much snow. Temperatures in the state can range from -60° F to over 100° F.

Cruisin' in Colorado!

Natural Resources

Many minerals are found in Colorado. These include molybdenum, zinc, copper, and silver. Sand, gravel, and stone are mined there, too. The state also has deposits of oil and natural gas.

Economy

As in most states, service jobs make up most of Colorado's economy. Nearly four fifths of Colorado's income comes from the service industry. Manufacturing is another major industry. One main product is science equipment. Food processing is also important. Factories make meat products, beer, and soft drinks.

Some people still farm. Major farm products are cattle, hay, wheat, sugar beets, and apples. Mining still supplies jobs for many Colorado people. Oil, natural gas, and coal are important products. Several military bases are located in Colorado, too.

Higher Education

Colorado has a variety of colleges and universities to attend. The University of Colorado was started in 1861. Its main campus is in Boulder. Fort Collins is the home of Colorado State University. It was founded in 1870.

Famous People

Many people from Colorado have gone on to make their mark on the world. Jack Dempsey, the world champion boxer, was from the state. John Denver, the popular singer, also had a home there. John Elway was the long-time quarterback for the Denver Broncos. Some cowboy poets have become well-known, too. Waddie Mitchell and Baxter Black write humorous poems about the cowboy way of life.

Colorado Today

Though Colorado has great beauty, it also has problems. Too many people want to enjoy the beauty. The  eastern slope of the Rockies is overcrowded with people. The mountain air and clear streams have become polluted. Now people in Colorado must work to preserve the beauty of their state.

COLORADO – The Centennial State

Assessment

Circle the letter of the correct answer.

1. The Pueblo Indians built their homes on _____.
   - **a.** rafts
   - **b.** cliffs
   - **c.** trains
   - **d.** trees

2. Spanish explorers came to Colorado searching for _____.
   - **a.** water
   - **b.** zinc
   - **c.** gold
   - **d.** buffalo

3. Trappers and fur traders in the Colorado area were known as _____.
   - **a.** river guys
   - **b.** ancient ones
   - **c.** Zuni
   - **d.** mountain men

4. The _____ are a major landform in Colorado.
   - **a.** Great Lakes
   - **b.** Coastal Plains
   - **c.** Rocky Mountains
   - **d.** Niagara Falls

Read each statement. Answer *true* or *false*.

_____ 5. The Dutch were the first Europeans to explore the Colorado area.

_____ 6. Denver was the first permanent town in Colorado.

_____ 7. Parts of Colorado were included in the Louisiana Purchase.

_____ 8. Colorado is known as the "Centennial State."

_____ 9. A drought struck Colorado in the 1930s.

COLORADO – *The Centennial State*

Travel Time!

Colorado is the "Rocky Mountain state." So there are plenty of camping and hiking places to go. Rocky Mountain National Park is one. It's near Estes Park, in north-central Colorado. The Royal Gorge, near Cañon City, is another wonderful sight to see. The gorge is a deep, narrow canyon cut by the Arkansas River. Its walls are more than 1,000 feet (300 m) tall. A railroad runs through the bottom of the gorge. A highway is built across the gorge. The bridge is 1,053 feet (321 m) above the river! Cañon City is in central Colorado, just northwest of Pueblo.

Mesa Verde National Park is another place to try. It is near Cortez, in the southwest corner of the state. For a change of pace, head to Great Sand Dunes National Monument. You can guess what you'll find there! It is near Alamosa, in south-central Colorado. And of course, there is always Pikes Peak. It is in central Colorado, just west of Colorado Springs.

If you like history, try Dinosaur National Monument. It features fossils and old dinosaur bones. It is in the northwest corner of the state. Buffalo Bill's grave can be seen on Lookout Mountain. It is near Golden, just west of Denver. And if you like money, there is the U.S. Mint in Denver. Coins are made there.

Colorado also has many annual outdoor activities. A dogsled race is held in Leadville each December. Leadville is in the Rocky Mountains in central Colorado. The Pikes Peak Auto Race is held in July. World Cup Ski Racing takes place in Aspen and Vail. These races occur in February and March. These towns are in the Rocky Mountains in central Colorado. The Pikes Peak or Bust Rodeo occurs in Denver each January. And a Winter Carnival takes place in February. It is held in Steamboat Springs, in northwest Colorado.

Whatever you decide to try, you will have a great time in Colorado.

Travel Time!

Pack Your Bags!

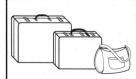

- Plan a hiking and climbing trip up Pikes Peak. The mountain is 14,110 feet (4,301 m) tall. How many miles tall is the peak? How long do you think it would take to climb the peak? Would you need special equipment? Write a diary page about your trip up the mountain. Draw a picture to go with your diary entry. (By the way, if you get tired, there are a road and a railroad that run up the mountain.)

On the Road!

- There are many places to snow-ski in Colorado. Find a road map of the state. Mark a route from your home to Aspen or Vail. How far is each place from your home? Driving 60 miles per hour, how long would you need to drive to get to each place?
- If you had a week to vacation in Aspen or Vail, what would you do? Plan a schedule for each day. How much do you think such a trip would cost? Don't forget hotel costs!

Snapshots!

- Draw a picture of yourself riding the train at the bottom of Royal Gorge. Or, draw a picture of yourself in a car crossing the bridge above Royal Gorge.
- What kind of dinosaurs lived in Colorado long ago? Draw a picture of one that might have lived there.
- Draw a picture of your family camping in the Rocky Mountains.

COLORADO – The Centennial State

State Your Facts!

Capital: Honolulu

Abbreviation: HI

Statehood: August 21, 1959—
the 50th state

Motto: *Ua mau ke ea o ka aina i ka
pono* ("The Life of the Land Is
Perpetuated in Righteousness")

Bird: Nene (Hawaiian goose)

Flower: Yellow hibiscus

Tree: Kukui

Area: 6,459 sq mi (16,729 sq km)—
47th in size

Five largest cities: Honolulu, Hilo,
Kailua, Kaneohe, Waipahu

Highest point: Mauna Kea—13,796 ft
(4,205 m)

Name _____ Date _____

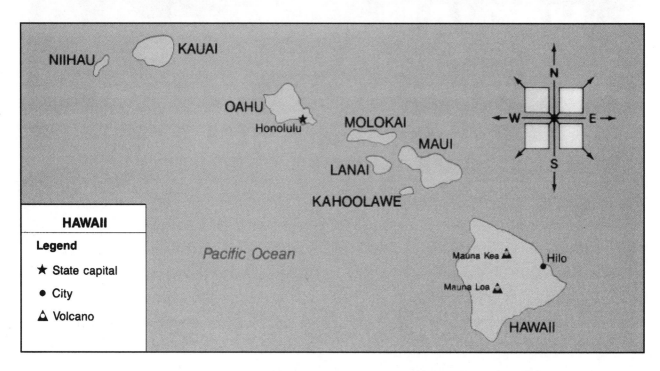

Intermediate directions are between the cardinal directions on a compass rose. Follow the directions below. Then fill in the blanks with cardinal or intermediate directions.

1. Finish the compass rose on the map above. Add the intermediate directions *NE*, *SE*, *SW*, and *NW*.

2. Find the island of Lanai on the map. Circle it.

3. Draw a line from Lanai to Maui.

   Maui is _____ of Lanai.

4. Draw a line from Lanai to the big island of Hawaii.

   Hawaii is _____ of Lanai.

5. Find the city of Hilo on the big island of Hawaii.

   Which volcano is southwest of Hilo? _____

   Which volcano is northwest of Hilo? _____

Hello from Hawaii!

Hawaii started as volcanoes. The island began forming under the ocean. Over millions of years, plants grew, animals found their way there, and people began to explore the beautiful islands.

History

People did not begin to visit the islands of Hawaii until 1,200 years ago. People from Tahiti and the surrounding islands built long boats. They left their islands to look for new lands. There is no written information about this exploration. The Polynesians did not write. However, they told stories that have been passed down from generation to generation.

Each island was ruled by a different group of natives. The islands had strict rules about how people could act. The people were put into a group, or a social order, depending on what family they lived in or what job they did. The most powerful people were royal. They made the laws. Other groups included servants and soldiers.

Captain James Cook was the first European explorer to visit the Hawaii islands. He was from England. He landed on the Kauai island in 1778. He called the new land *Sandwich Islands* in honor of the Earl of Sandwich. The Earl of Sandwich was head of the British Navy. Captain Cook soon left the islands, but came back again the next year. The people living on the island thought he had taken a boat. The islanders killed Captain Cook and some of his crew.

For a time, the Europeans did not return to Hawaii. But its location between Asia and America made it a good place to stop on long journeys. Traders discovered goods on the island that they could sell in other parts of the world. Soon, missionaries began to visit the land. Missionaries were people who taught others about Christianity. The Hawaiians believed in many gods. Some of the people listened about Christianity. Others kept believing in their gods.

The traders and missionaries brought a problem to the islanders. They brought disease. The native people on the islands could not fight the diseases. They had no medicines. Nearly 300,000 of the islanders died.

HAWAII – *The Aloha State*

Hello from Hawaii!

The people on different islands fought one another. By 1810, King Kamehameha I won control of all the islands. He used guns traders brought from Europe. Upon his death, Kamehameha's son, Kamehameha II, became the ruler. Kamehameha II

liked the ways of the traders. He led the way for his people to accept Christianity. Soon the natives learned to read and write. They built schools, stores, and churches. Kamehameha III began a system of government. The rules and laws followed the ones in the United States *Constitution*. But the king was still the most powerful person on the island.

The first sugarcane plantation was started in 1835 by a group of Americans. It was a success. Soon, many other businesses followed. Pineapple plantations became as important as sugarcane plantations. The native population was small due to disease. So the companies brought in workers from other countries. Many immigrants came from China, Japan, and Korea. Soon, the native people were outnumbered. The plantation owners fought the Hawaiian king, Kalakaua, to gain power. By 1895, Hawaii was thought of as a country. Two years later, it became a territory of the United States.

Because of Hawaii's location, the United States built several naval bases in the area. One was built at Pearl Harbor, Oahu. In World War II, Japan and the United States argued. Japan made a surprise attack at Pearl Harbor on December 7, 1941. It caused much destruction. Japan and the United States went to war.

After the war, many people heard of the beauty of Hawaii. Visitors began to travel there. In 1959, Hawaii became the 50th state to join the United States. It has since become a major tourist spot for people all over the world. But Hawaii has faced several problems. Workers on plantations have asked for more pay and fewer working hours. To get the

Hello from Hawaii!

plantation owners to listen, they decided not to work for several days. Also, in 1975, two earthquakes and a major tidal wave hit Hawaii. Many people were hurt, and much property was damaged. In 1992, a hurricane passed over the land, causing more property damage. Each time, the people of Hawaii worked together to rebuild.

Landscape

There are 132 islands that form the state of Hawaii. From north to south the islands extend 230 miles (370 km). They are 350 miles (565 km) wide from east to west. Landscape ranges from high mountains and deep valleys to tropical forests and deserts. The mountains are formed from volcanoes, some of which still shoot ash and flow lava. The coastline is 750 miles (1,207 km) long.

Climate

Hawaii has a mild climate for most of the year. Average temperatures range from 72° F to 79° F, no matter the season. However, most temperatures in Hawaii can vary with the landscape. Rainfall also varies. Winds blowing off the ocean and toward the mountains cause much rain. Average rainfall is 100 inches. On the other side of the mountains, there may be little rain.

Natural Resources

Since Hawaii is a new island, it has few natural resources. There are no large rivers or lakes. The islands do have such minerals as gravel, pumice, and clay. The beauty of the land is its greatest resource.

Economy

Most of the state has a year-round growing season. Pineapple, sugarcane, and macadamia nuts are important crops. Out of these foods has come another industry— food processing. Pineapple is canned, and sugarcane is made into sugar and other products. Hawaii's location and mild climate also make it a perfect vacation spot.

HAWAII – The Aloha State

Hello from Hawaii!

Visitors from all over the world visit all year long. Many Hawaiians work in restaurants, hotels, and entertainment to make the stay pleasant.

Higher Education

Hawaii has several colleges. The University of Hawaii is the biggest. It has several branches at different places around the state. Some of the branches are two-year community colleges. Other places are research schools for the movement of the Earth, ocean life, and the observation of the sky.

include Duke Kahanamoku and Don Ho. Kahanamoku won a gold medal in swimming in the 1920 Olympics and helped start surfing as a sport. Don Ho is a well-known singer that tourists like to see.

Famous People

Bernice Pauahi Bishop was related to King Kamehameha I. She could have been a queen of Hawaii. However, she did not want to be queen. Bishop married an American businessman. She thought it was important to remember the Hawaiian culture. She made a museum that told about the history of Hawaii. She also wanted schools to be in Hawaii. When she died, her husband gave money to build two schools. Other famous Hawaiians

Hawaii Today

People will always visit Hawaii because of the climate and the beauty of the land. But the state faces problems due to the number of visitors. Fresh water on some islands is in short supply. Hotels and businesses build in places that take land from plants and animals. Many kinds of plants and animals are endangered. The people see the problems and are working to pass laws to protect these important parts of Hawaii.

Assessment

Write the correct words to complete the sentences.

1. Hawaii's nickname is "The

   _____ State."

2. The capital of Hawaii is

   _____.

3. The Hawaii islands were formed by

   _____.

4. Many native people on Hawaii died from

   _____ the Europeans brought.

5. King Kumehameha I was the first ruler to win control of all the

   _____.

6. The Japanese attacked the navy base at

   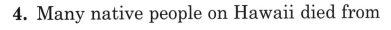 

   Oahu, in 1941.

7. Sugarcane and _____ are important crops
   grown in Hawaii.

8. Duke Kahanamoku won an Olympic medal in swimming and helped

   start _____ as a sport.

Name _____ Date _____

Travel Time!

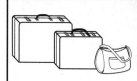

Pack Your Bags!

You will need:
- a state map
- resource books

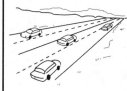

On the Road!

- Hawaii has 750 miles of coastline. This includes the coastline all around the 132 islands. Suppose you wanted to walk around all the islands. How long would it take you? What would you need to pack for the trip? Make a plan for your trip. The questions below will help you.

- How many miles could you walk in one hour? _____

- How many miles could you walk in one day? _____

  Based on your data above, how long would it take you

  walk all around the coast of the islands? _____

- What will you pack for your trip? Remember that you will be on the beach.

Snapshots

- Draw a picture of yourself on your trip on a separate sheet of paper. On the back of your picture, write a journal entry describing what you see.

IDAHO
The Gem State

Boise
★
IDAHO

≡ State Your Facts! ≡

Capital: Boise

Abbreviation: ID

Statehood: July 3, 1890—
the 43rd state

Motto: *Esto Perpetua* ("It is perpetual")

Bird: Mountain bluebird

Flower: Syringa

Tree: White pine

Area: 83,574 sq mi (216,456 sq km)—
13th in size

Five largest cities: Boise, Pocatello,
Idaho Falls, Nampa, Lewiston

Highest point: Borah Peak—12,662 ft
(3,859 m)

Name _____ Date _____

Things To Do!

1. A globe is like a map on a ball. A globe usually has a distance scale in its key. But it is hard to use a ruler to measure distance on a globe. The map curves like a ball. Use a piece of string instead. Measure how far your town is from the following places. Write your answers in the chart below. Give your answer in both miles and kilometers.

Place	Miles	Kilometers
Honolulu, Hawaii		
Anchorage, Alaska		
Bangor, Maine		
Miami, Florida		
Washington, D.C.		
Paris, France		
Sydney, Australia		
Cape Town, South Africa		
Rio de Janeiro, Brazil		

2. Research the history of the state flag. Write a report about what you learn. When was the flag first made? What do the colors or pictures mean? Include a picture of the flag with your report.

3. Find out about an environmental problem in the state. Make a poster that tells about the problem. Include some pictures. How can the problem be fixed?

4. Learn the state song. Sing it for your class.

An Eyeful of Idaho!

People from Idaho have many bragging rights. Their state has the deepest canyon in the U.S. They have the longest river completely inside a state. They have one of the tallest waterfalls in the world. And they grow the most potatoes in the country.

History

Idaho was one of the last wildernesses in the U.S. Many American Indian groups lived in the area. The Nez Percé, Kutenai, and Coeur d'Alene groups lived in the north part of the area. The Paiute and Shoshone lived in the south part. All these groups raised horses. They used the horses to hunt buffalo. They also fished and hunted small game. They gathered wild plants, seeds, and nuts, too.

In 1803, the U.S. bought a very large piece of land from France. This was called the Louisiana Purchase. The land included Idaho. Fur traders began to move into the area around 1811. Many more came in the 1820s.

In 1855, a religious group called the Mormons arrived in Idaho. Many of the Mormons went on to Utah. But many stayed in Idaho to farm and colonize. In 1860, Mormons started the settlement of Franklin. This was the region's first permanent European town.

Also that year, gold was discovered in north-central Idaho. Thousands of gold seekers entered the area. The gold rush was on! By 1863, there were 70,000 settlers in the region. By 1870, though, the gold rush ended. Many people left. Only 15,000 settlers remained in the area.

More settlers arrived in the 1870s. To make room for them, the U.S. government made treaties with the Indians. The government said the Indians could have land elsewhere if they moved. The Indians were moved to reservations. Many of these places were barren. The land could not support the Indians. Sometimes the Indians left the reservations to find food. Often they were captured or killed for doing so. Most of the conflicts with the Indians ended in the late 1800s. Idaho became a state in 1890. In 1896, Idaho women were given the right to vote.

In the 1900s, the logging industry grew in the state. Mining became important, too. Many farms

IDAHO – The Gem State

An Eyeful of Idaho!

were started. In the 1950s and 1960s, more people moved to the state. Manufacturing grew into an important industry.

In 1976, a disaster occurred. Teton Dam, in southeast Idaho, collapsed. Billions of gallons of water flooded places downstream. Much property was damaged, and 11 people died.

Now, people in Idaho are working to preserve their wilderness areas. They are passing laws to protect nature. They want to brag about their state's beauty in the 21st century.

Landscape

Idaho is an odd-shaped, mountainous state. Its western border is like a long neck. The rest of the state looks like a pan. The long part is called a "panhandle." Idaho measures 483 miles (778 km) north to south along the panhandle. The state is 316 miles (509 km) wide in its southern part.

The north part of the state is very mountainous. The middle part is wild and primitive. It has deep canyons and tall mountains. Altogether, Idaho has 22 mountain ranges. Some of these are the Clearwater Mountains, the Salmon River Mountains, and the Sawtooth Mountains. South of the Sawtooth Mountains are the Snake River plains. This sloping plateau has forests and lakes. In the southwest part are desert uplands.

Two large rivers in the state are the Snake River and the Salmon River. The Snake is the larger river. But the Salmon River is the longest river in the U.S. that lies completely within one state's borders.

Climate

The winds off the Pacific Ocean and the many mountains work together to give Idaho a moderate climate. Temperatures are cooler at higher levels. Snow falls somewhere in the state every month of the year. Some places get over 200 inches of snow a year. In Idaho, more rain falls in the winter months. The summer months are the driest.

Natural Resources

In the 1860s through the 1880s, several gold strikes occurred in Idaho. Now the main things mined are silver, copper, gold, and

An Eyeful of Idaho!

phosphate rock. The many forests supply trees for lumber and wood products. The state uses its rivers to make hydroelectric power and to irrigate farmland.

Economy

You might think Idaho only makes money from its potatoes. The state is the leading producer of potatoes in the U.S. But the farms there also grow hay, barley, and sugar beets. Ranchers raise cattle and sheep, mostly for meat and wool. Manufacturing is an important industry in Idaho, too.

Service jobs keep many Idaho citizens busy. The service industry provides two thirds of Idaho's income. Service people help other people. Many Idaho service people now help tourists. Many more people now visit the state to explore the Idaho wilderness.

Higher Education

Idaho offers several major colleges and universities. The University of Idaho was started in 1889. Its main campus now is in Moscow. Idaho State University was founded in 1901. Its main campus is in Pocatello.

Famous People

Two famous people in history are connected to Idaho. Sacagawea served as a guide for Lewis and Clark on their expedition. Chief Joseph of the Nez Percé did not want his people to lose their freedom. They were being forced to live on a reservation in Idaho. Joseph led his people toward Canada. But federal troops captured them. Joseph and his people were forced to return to the reservation.

The famous writer Ernest Hemingway lived in Idaho for many years. One of his most famous novels is *The Old Man and the Sea.*

Idaho Today

People in Idaho have a tough choice. They want to preserve the Idaho wilderness. But they also need progress in their state. Perhaps they can find the right balance in the 21st century.

IDAHO – *The Gem State*

Assessment

Circle the letter of the correct answer.

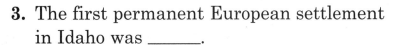

1. American Indian groups in Idaho used horses to hunt _____.
   a. ducks   **b.** trains
   c. buffalo   **d.** salmon

2. Idaho was part of the _____.
   a. Big Land Buy
   b. Louisiana Purchase
   c. Texas Trade
   d. Denver Deal

3. The first permanent European settlement in Idaho was _____.
   a. Franklin   **b.** Joseph
   c. Meriwether   **d.** Teton City

4. In 1896, Idaho women won the right to _____.
   a. work   **b.** complain
   c. vote   **d.** ride horses

5. In 1976, Teton _____ collapsed.
   a. Bridge   **b.** Center
   c. Tower   **d.** Dam

6. _____ was a guide for the Lewis and Clark expedition.
   a. Pocahontas
   b. Daniel Boone
   c. Sacagawea
   d. Ida Home

7. Idaho is the leading producer of _____ in the U.S.
   a. gold   **b.** potatoes
   c. wool   **d.** barley

Travel Time!

Where to go in Idaho? If you like nature or camping, you have many choices. The state has 16 large national forests. Idaho also boasts 22 state parks and three huge wilderness areas. There are also many rivers that offer white-water rafting and canoeing. The middle fork of the Salmon River is one favorite. It is sometimes called the River of No Return. It is located in northwest Idaho.

The Snake River is another favorite river for boaters. On the western border of Idaho, this river has cut a deep canyon. Called Hells Canyon, it is the deepest canyon in the U.S. It is about 7,900 feet (2,407 m) deep. In southern Idaho, the Snake turns east. There you can find Shoshone Falls. It is one of the tallest waterfalls in the world.

Another nature place to visit is the Craters of the Moon National Monument. This area was once full of active volcanoes. Now there are old volcano cones and craters. The area, in central Idaho, looks much like the Moon's surface.

For cold weather activities, try the Crystal Ice Cave. It is near American Falls, in southeast

Idaho. It is about 40 miles (56 km) west of Pocatello. If you like snow skiing, head to Sun Valley Ski and Resort Area. Sun Valley is just south of the Sawtooth Mountains. It is about 4 miles (6.4 km) southwest of Ketchum.

There are many other things to do in Idaho. The Teton Flood Museum is in Rexburg. This is in eastern Idaho. The Lionel Hampton Jazz Festival is held in Moscow each February. Moscow is in the panhandle of Idaho. Lumberjack Days are held in Orofino each September. Orofino is also in the panhandle part of the state.

And who can forget the glorious potato? Attend Idaho Spud Day. It is held in Shelley each September. Shelley is in southeast Idaho, near Pocatello. Or you just might like the World Potato Exposition. It is held in Blackfoot, which is also near Pocatello.

IDAHO – The Gem State

Name _____   Date _____

Travel Time!

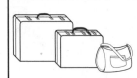

Pack Your Bags!

- You have ten days to travel around Idaho. Would you like to camp out, go boating, listen to music, or what? First, make a list of things you would like to do. Then make a list of places in Idaho you can do those things. Use the article on page 55 for ideas.
- Now plan a schedule for each of the ten days. Where will you go? What route will you take? Find a road map of Idaho. Use it to plan your routes. Where will you stay? Will you camp out or stay in hotels?
- Plan a budget for each day. How much do you think you will have to spend each day on your vacation? What would be the total cost for your ten-day trip?

Snapshots!

- Chief Joseph was a leader of the Nez Percé Indians. He did not want his people to lose their freedom. In 1877, Joseph led his people from Oregon toward Canada. But they were captured. When captured, Joseph said, "I am tired of fighting. . . . It is cold and we have no blankets. The little children are freezing. We have no food. . . . My heart is sick and sad. From where the Sun now stands, I will fight no more forever." After his capture, Joseph and his group were sent to reservations. Joseph died in 1904. It is said he died of a "broken heart" for his lost homeland.
- Write a poem about this great chief. Draw a picture of him, too.

IDAHO – The Gem State

NEVADA
The Silver State

Carson City
NEVADA

State Your Facts!

Capital: Carson City

Abbreviation: NV

Statehood: October 31, 1864—
the 36th state

Motto: "All for Our Country"

Bird: Mountain bluebird

Flower: Sagebrush

Tree: Bristlecone pine and single-leaf piñon

Area: 110,561 sq mi (286,352 sq km)—
7th in size

Five largest cities: Las Vegas, Reno,
Henderson, Sparks, North
Las Vegas

Highest point: Boundary Peak—
13,140 ft (4,005 m)

Things To Do!

Look at the map. Read the directions. Write the names on the map to locate places in Nevada.

1. Reno is located on the *Truckee River*.

2. The *Colorado River* flows along the southeast border of Nevada.

3. *Great Basin National Park* is south of Ruth.

4. *Black Rock Desert* is found in the northwest corner of the state.

5. *Lake Tahoe* is west of Carson City.

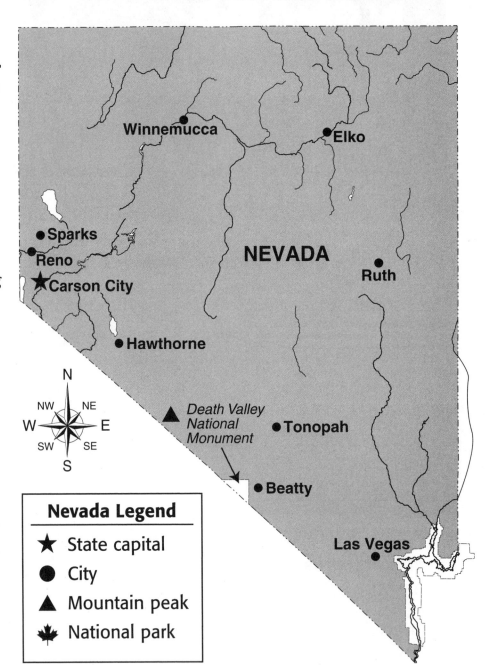

Nevada Legend

★ State capital
● City
▲ Mountain peak
🍁 National park

6. The *Humboldt River* runs through the cities of Winnemucca and Elko.

7. Hawthorne is southeast of *Walker Lake*.

8. *Boundary Peak* is on the southwest border of Nevada directly west of Tonopah.

Notes on Nevada!

Nevada was one of the last areas to be explored. High mountains and deserts kept travelers away. Nevada is now one of the most popular vacation spots, calling thousands to visit its cities and mountains for entertainment.

History

The Pueblo were the first known people to live in Nevada. They built huge communities. They farmed by the rivers. For some unknown reason, the people disappeared. Later, three groups of Native Americans called the rough land home. Some lived in the desert, and some by the lakes and rivers.

Europeans began to explore the area in the late 1700s. The Spanish missionary, Father Francisco Garcés, is thought to be the first one to arrive. Other explorers followed more slowly. The mountains were high, and the deserts were large. Beginning in the 1830s, the United States government paid explorers to make trails for people who traveled from the east coast to California.

The United States and Mexico fought a war in 1846. They argued

over the boundaries between the countries. The war lasted two years. The United States won. The U.S. claimed much of the land, including present-day Nevada and seven other states.

The gold rush soon began in California. Fortune seekers crossed through Nevada. They did not stay, though. The first permanent town was not started until 1861 by the Mormons. The Mormons were a religious group. Other people did not understand the Mormons' beliefs. The small group packed their belongings to find a new place. They settled in Nevada in 1849. Within six years, they had built a mission in Las Vegas.

Miners found silver in 1859. The find was called the Comstock Lode. People came from the East and West to set up silver mines. In 1861, Nevada became a territory of the United States. The Native Americans living in the

NEVADA – *The Silver State*

territory became angry. The trees were being cut. Their hunting grounds were being destroyed. The settlers and natives attacked each other. The settlers asked the army for help. The army came and killed many natives in one village.

The Civil War had started in the East. The Union needed people to fight and money to pay for it. Nevada did not have enough people to become a state. However, the government decided to make Nevada a state. They felt that with the discovery of silver, many people would move to Nevada. On October 31, 1864, Nevada became the 36th state. The Union won the Civil War six months later.

People flooded the West. Many mined for silver and gold. Towns were built overnight. By 1880, there was a crash. The Comstock Lode had run out of silver. It closed. Other smaller mines did, too. People left quickly. Towns became ghost towns. Some people began cattle and sheep ranches. The valleys in the mountains were rich in grass for the animals. Again, bad fortune hit the state. Cattle were killed when there were several years of cold winters

and hot summers. Shipping the animals by rail was expensive.

The Native Americans across the land were being treated unfairly. They were being moved. Their hunting grounds were destroyed. Wovoka, a Native Indian, had a vision of a dance from the Great Spirit. It was called the Ghost Dance. Wovoka's followers believed this dance would help them regain their land and scare away the settlers. The United States government outlawed the dance. The Sioux in South Dakota did not listen. The army attacked them, killing 150 people.

In 1900, mining again became important. Other minerals were found, such as copper and zinc. The mines helped supply needs for World War I. Just as in 1880, fortune changed. The mines went dry, and the Great Depression hit the country. People were out of work. They had no money. Nevada

Notes on Nevada!

people tried to keep going. They decided to make gambling legal, the first state to do so. The Hoover Dam was also built. It supplied water to farms and much-needed electricity to the whole state.

In the last 50 years, Nevada has created special interests that attract people from all over the  nation. Gambling and entertainment in Las Vegas draw millions of people. Also, the state is home to the Atomic Energy Commission. Nuclear weapons are tested in underground areas. Many people are afraid of the effects of radiation. Despite numerous protests, Nevada continues the work. Today, it is the fastest growing state in the nation.

Landscape

The land varies greatly from mountains to deserts. The Rocky Mountains run through most of the state. This area is known as the Great Basin. Most of the mountains are covered in pine forests. Deep valleys and canyons dot the land. Deserts are found on the northwest and southeast corners of the state. Throughout Nevada, geysers and hot springs are plentiful.

Climate

The mountains in Oregon and California block the winds blowing east. Thus, Nevada does not get much rain. Average rainfall for the state is about eight inches. Because of the variety of landforms, temperatures also vary. Average temperature is 32° F in January and 68° F in July. Desert temperatures have been as high as 122° F.

Natural Resources

The history of Nevada is tied to the large number of minerals in the state. Most of the silver is gone, but the state still mines copper, gold, mercury, and turquoise. Some mountains are covered in trees. While some trees are cut for lumber, many are protected in national parks.

Notes on Nevada!

Economy

Nevada attracts a large number of tourists. Almost half of the workers have jobs in service to meet the needs of the visitors. They work in hotels, restaurants, casinos, and entertainment clubs. Mining is also an important business. Some ranching of cattle and sheep provides additional money for the state.

Higher Education

There are two schools of higher learning in Nevada. The University of Nevada was started in 1874 at Elko. It moved one year later to Reno. It is known for its research in mining and the desert. Sierra Nevada College was formed in 1969. It offers a four-year degree in liberal arts.

Famous People

William Lear was born in Nevada. He developed a company  that built small private jets. Liberace also called Nevada home. He was known for playing the piano while wearing decorative costumes. Finally, Samuel Clemens, better known as Mark Twain, spent several of his adult years in Nevada. Some of the books he wrote dealt with his experiences there.

Nevada Today

From the beginning, Nevada's history has been tied to the ups and downs of the mines. Since the state is so rich in a variety of minerals, mining is still important today. However, just as a majority of the silver ran out in the 1800s, there is a limited supply. Nevada watches the amount mined each year.

People are moving to Nevada in record numbers. Nevada faces many problems with these people. Water has always been in short supply. Nevada is concerned that it may run out of water. Pollution is another worry. The state has begun to pass laws to control pollution. Finally, the testing of nuclear weapons raises many questions. How safe is it? What long-term effects, if any, will there be? Nevada people continue to work to solve the problems, and surely they will as they have in the past.

Assessment

Read each statement. Answer *true* or *false*.

_____ 1. The Pueblo were the first group to live in Nevada.

_____ 2. A Spanish missionary is thought to be the first European to see the area of Nevada.

_____ 3. The United States fought with Spain to win control of the land that included Nevada.

_____ 4. The Comstock Lode was a famous gold mine.

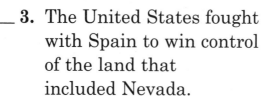

_____ 5. Las Vegas was settled by the Mormons.

_____ 6. The state receives an average of eight inches of rain a year.

_____ 7. Fishing is an important source of money for the state.

_____ 8. Mark Twain lived in Nevada for several years.

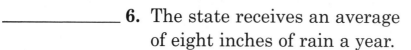

Travel Time!

Pack Your Bags!

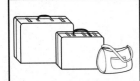

You will need:
- a state map
- resource books

On the Road!

- Nevada has many national and state parks. Some have interesting landscapes. Some are recreation areas for swimming and boating. Others have fossil imprints. Research to find one that you would like to visit. Then answer the questions below on another sheet of paper.

1. What park did you choose?
2. What is the nearest city or town?
3. What will visitors see in this park?
4. What kinds of animals or wildlife might live in this park?
5. What can visitors do while visiting the park?
6. Why do you want to visit this park?

Snapshots

- Draw a picture of yourself in the park you choose. Be sure to include a picture that shows the reason you want to visit.

NEVADA – *The Silver State*

Name _____ Date _____

OREGON
The Beaver State

★ Salem

OREGON

☰ State Your Facts! ☰

Capital: Salem

Abbreviation: OR

Statehood: February 14, 1859—
the 33rd state

Motto: *Alis Volat Propriis* ("She flies
with her own wings")

Bird: Western meadowlark

Flower: Oregon grape

Tree: Douglas fir

Area: 97,052 sq mi (251,365 sq km)—
10th in size

Five largest cities: Portland, Eugene,
Salem, Gresham, Beaverton

Highest point: Mount Hood—11,239 ft
(3,426 m)

Sports teams: Portland Trailblazers (basketball)

Things To Do!

1. Most globes and world maps have a grid of lines on them. The lines that run east and west are called *lines of latitude*. The Equator is a line of latitude. It is called 0° (zero degrees). The area north of the Equator is called the Northern Hemisphere. The area south of the Equator is called the Southern

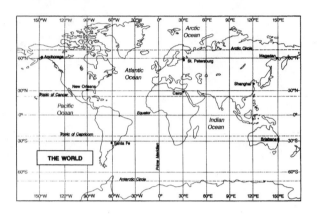

Hemisphere. Lines of latitude north of the Equator are marked with an *N*. The North Pole is 90° N. Lines south of the Equator are marked with an *S*. The South Pole is 90° S.

The lines that run north and south are called *lines of longitude*. The Prime Meridian is a line of longitude. It is in Great Britain. The area east of this line is called the Eastern Hemisphere. To the west of this line is the Western Hemisphere. Lines of longitude east of this line are marked with an *E*. Lines to the west of this line are marked with a *W*.

Find the lines of latitude and longitude near your town. Use the lines to estimate your town's location. When you write latitude and longitude, you write the line of latitude first. For example, the latitude and longitude for Florence, Oregon, is about 44° N, 124° W. Write the latitude and longitude of your town.

2. Now follow the line of latitude near your town east or west. Find a big city somewhere in the world that is near that line. Write the name of the city. Now follow the line of longitude near your town north or south. Find a city somewhere in the world near that line. Write the name of the city.

3. Get your teacher or an adult to help you with this activity. Write down the latitude and longitude for your town. Then go on the Internet. Go to this address: **http://www.fourmilab.ch/cgi-bin/uncgi/Earth**

This is the web address for EarthCam. At this site you can type in your latitude and longitude. Then you can see your area from a camera in space!

On the Loose in Oregon!

In the late 1800s, the promise of a better life lay in the name *Oregon*. Now, we are moving into the 21st century. The efforts of the people of Oregon still offer the promise of a better life.

History

The first people in Oregon were American Indians. By 1500, over 100 groups lived in the area. The largest group was the Chinook. They lived in northwest Oregon, near the mouth of the Columbia River. They fished for food. The Nez Percé group lived to the east of the Chinook. This group was the first to raise horses. They also fished for food in the Columbia River.

In the late 1700s, European and American explorers began to arrive. British explorer James Cook visited the area in 1778. Ten years later, Robert Gray arrived by ship from the east coast of the U.S. Then, in 1805, Meriwether Lewis and William Clark explored the area. President Thomas Jefferson wanted them to find a land route to the Pacific Ocean. With the help of the Nez Percé, Lewis and Clark were able to do so.

Soon, fur traders moved into the Oregon Country. Later, in the 1840s, settlers began to arrive.

They came along the Oregon Trail. This trail had been used  by trappers heading west. It started in Independence, Missouri. It stretched across the Great Plains and the Rocky Mountains. The trail ended in the Oregon Country. The first wagon train, with over 1,000 settlers, arrived in 1843. By 1845, over 5,000 settlers lived in the Williamette Valley.

The American Indians in the area did not like the new settlers. Their hunting and fishing areas were threatened. The settlers brought many diseases, too. Many Indians died from the diseases. The U.S. government began to pressure the Indians, too. It wanted the Indians to move to land set aside for them called *reservations*. Often the reservations were in bad locations.

All these problems caused the Indians to fight back. Many wars followed. The last major Indian battle in Oregon was the Nez Percé War. The Nez Percé did not want to go to a reservation. In May 1877, Chief Joseph led a group of 800 toward Canada. Federal troops pursued them. The group was captured in Montana in September

OREGON – *The Beaver State*

On the Loose in Oregon!

1877. Chief Joseph and his followers were sent to a reservation. Joseph died there in 1904.

In the 1860s, railroads made their way into Oregon. This helped to improve trade. In 1873, farmers formed the Oregon State Grange. This group worked to end the railroads' high shipping fees.

Through the 20th century, manufacturing grew in Oregon. Oregon factories made many items to help in World War II. The logging industry prospered in the 1950s and 1960s, too. But then the demand for wood products went down. People are also worried that too much logging destroys the homes of many animals. In the later part of the 20th century, Oregon has passed many laws to protect the environment.

Landscape

Oregon is one of the larger states. It measures about 294 miles (473 km) north to south. It is about 401 miles (645 km) wide. It also has about 296 miles (476 km) of coastline on the Pacific Ocean. Oregon is a state of mountains, fertile valleys, and high plateaus.

As in Washington, the Cascade Mountains divide the state of Oregon. Far west of the Cascades is the Coastal Range.  It has heavy forests and a few sandy beaches. Most of the bays along the coast are shallow. They do not make good harbors. Between the Coastal Range and the Cascades is the Williamette Valley. It contains good, fertile farmland. Most of Oregon's large cities are in this valley. Half of the state's residents live there.

The Cascades form the eastern wall of the valley. East of the Cascades is a variety of landscapes. There are desert plains and hills with lush forests. There are deep canyons and tall waterfalls. The Blue Mountains cover much of northeast Oregon. The Harney Basin in southeast Oregon is much like a desert.

Climate

The Cascades also divide Oregon into two climate zones. On the coast the weather is mild and humid. Average rainfall is about 80 inches a year. The Williamette Valley also has a mild climate. The valley gets little snow, and it has a long growing season.

On the Loose in Oregon!

In the Cascades, the climate varies widely. It goes from mild and damp on the western slope to constant ice on the peaks. In southeast Oregon, the climate is semi-arid. Very little rain falls there.

Natural Resources

Most of Oregon's natural resources are found in the western part of the state. The many forests west of the Cascades provide timber for logging. The Pacific Ocean supplies much seafood. Dams on the Columbia River produce hydroelectric power. Sand, gravel, limestone, gold, silver, copper, and bauxite are mined in the state.

Economy

Oregon's natural resources provide many jobs. Many people work in mining, logging, and fishing. Others work on farms. Oregon's main crop is wheat. Manufacturing is also important in the state. Wood products are the main thing made.

Service jobs are a growing part of the economy. Many people work in wholesale and retail sales. Others have jobs as doctors, social workers, clerks, or lawyers. Many other people work to help tourists who visit the state on vacation.

Higher Education

Oregon has a variety of colleges and universities from which to choose. Oregon State University was started in 1868. It is located in Corvallis. The University of Oregon has its main campus in Eugene. It was founded in 1876.

Famous People

Oregon has been the home to several famous writers. Beverly Cleary is a famous writer of children's books. Most young people know some of her characters, such as Ramona Quimby. Another famous writer is Ursula LeGuin. She writes science fiction stories.

Oregon Today

Oregon is known as a beautiful place to live. Going into the 21st century, Oregon people are working to keep that belief true.

OREGON – *The Beaver State*

Assessment

Circle the letter of the correct answer.

1. Two large groups of American Indians in Oregon were the _____.
   a. Cherokee and Modoc
   b. Chinook and Nez Percé
   c. Apache and Seminole
   d. Klamath and Algonquin

2. Many settlers reached Oregon by traveling along the _____.
   a. Wilderness Road   b. Trail of Tears
   c. Pony Express   d. Oregon Trail

3. Most of Oregon's large cities are in the _____.
   a. Cascade Mountains
   b. desert
   c. Williamette Valley
   d. Blue Mountains

4. Beverly Cleary is a famous _____.
   a. writer   b. painter
   c. chief   d. cook

Number the events in the order they happened.

_____ Captain James Cook explored the area in 1778.

_____ The Oregon State Grange was formed.

_____ Lewis and Clark explored the Oregon area.

_____ Oregon factories made items to help in World War II.

_____ Chief Joseph and his group were captured in 1877.

_____ The first wagon train reached the Oregon Country.

Travel Time!

Oregon is known as a beautiful place to live. It is also a beautiful place to visit. Camping and hiking are two major activities in the state. The Cascade Mountains offer many places to do these things. On Oregon's northern border are two good sites. The Columbia River Gorge and Mount Hood show you the lows and highs of the state. These two are about 60 miles (96 km) east and southeast of Portland. Portland is in northwest Oregon, on the Columbia River.

Crater Lake National Park is another good place to visit. It is 90 miles (145 km) southeast of Eugene. Eugene is in west-central Oregon, near the Williamette River. The park features a lake in the bowl of a dead volcano. You can learn all about volcanoes at this park.

Near Portland is Multnomah Falls. It is one of the nation's highest waterfalls. Its water drops over 600 feet (183 m). For another outdoor spot, visit Hells Canyon National Recreation Area near La Grande. This is in the Blue Mountains in northeast Oregon. There are also many other state parks and forests throughout the state.

The coast also offers many chances for fun and adventure. There are many recreation sites for camping, hiking, and water activities. Florence has two good places to visit. Sea Lions Cave is the home of many sea lions. Visitors travel 2,000 feet (610 m) down in an elevator to reach the cave. Also in Florence is the Heceta Head Lighthouse. Florence is on the coast, west of Eugene. If you want to learn about sea life, head to the Oregon State Aquarium. It is on the coast in Newport, about 45 miles (72 km) north of Florence.

If you want to explore frontier or American Indian life, Oregon has several places to visit. The Pendleton Roundup is one of the most famous rodeos in the country. It features rodeo contests and traditional Indian dancing events. The Roundup is every September in Pendleton, in northeast Oregon. The Tygh Valley All-Indian Rodeo is held in May at The Dalles. The Dalles is in northwest Oregon, about 75 miles (120 km) east of Portland.

Or you might want to visit the Warm Springs Indian Reservation.

OREGON – The Beaver State

Travel Time!

It is in northwest Oregon, about 75 miles (120 km) southeast of Portland. The Oregon Trail Pageant is held in July and August in Oregon City. This is in northwest Oregon, just southeast of Portland. Or if you enjoy logging excitement, head to the World Championship Timber Carnival. It is held each July in Albany. Albany is in northwest Oregon, about 60 miles (96 km) south of Portland.

Oregon's beauty calls to you. Come take a look.

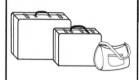

Pack Your Bags!

- Find a road map of Oregon. Then draw your own map of the state. Show the major highways on your map. Which roads would you use to go from your home to Pendleton? Color those roads blue. Which roads would you use to go from your home to the state capital? Color those roads red. What is the state capital of Oregon?
- Find a map of Oregon. Find 20 cities or towns in the state. Then write the names of those places in ABC order.

On the Road!

- Which of the places on your list would you like to visit? Why? Write a short paper telling your reasons. How far is the place from your home? How much do you think a bus ticket to go there would cost?

Snapshots!

- Write a story about being lost off the coast of Oregon. Then you see the light at Heceta Head Lighthouse. You know you are saved. Draw a picture of the lighthouse to go with your story.
- Draw a picture of yourself as a rodeo rider.
- Draw a picture of some tall waterfalls.

OREGON – The Beaver State

State Your Facts!

Capital: Salt Lake City

Abbreviation: UT

Statehood: January 4, 1896—
the 45th state

Motto: "Industry"

Bird: Seagull

Flower: Sego lily

Tree: Blue spruce

Area: 84,905 sq mi (219,902 sq km)—
11th in size

Five largest cities: Salt Lake City, West
Valley City, Provo, Sandy, Orem

Highest point: Kings Point—13,528 ft
(4,123 m)

Sports teams: Utah Jazz (basketball), Utah
Starzz (women's basketball)

Name _____ Date _____

Look at the map of Utah. Then answer the questions.

1. Which mountains
   stretch between
   about 41° N and
   42° N latitude?

   _____

   _____

2. What is the labeled
   line of longitude
   touching Zion
   National Park?

   _____

   _____

3. What lake is about
   40° N latitude?

   _____

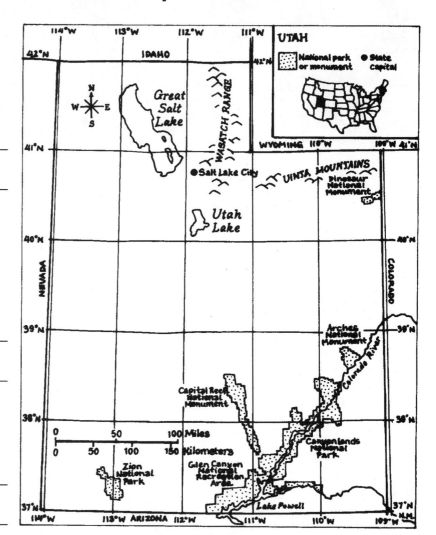

4. Which two parks or monuments are at about 111° W longitude?

   _____

   _____

5. What large lake touches the latitude line 41° N?

   _____

You Can Visit Utah!

Utah is a rugged but beautiful state. It has snow-covered mountains. It has wind-blown canyons. It even has a desert made of salt. You can go visit Utah to see it all!

History

A number of Native American nations lived in Utah. Among them were the Paiute, Shoshone, and the Ute, the group for which Utah was named. Europeans did not arrive until 1776, the year that the east coast states claimed their independence from England. The explorers were two Spanish priests. Nearly 75 years passed before other explorers visited the area. Trappers, known as mountain men, hunted small animals all through the Rocky Mountains.

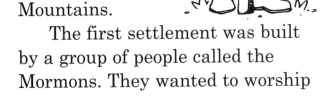

The first settlement was built by a group of people called the Mormons. They wanted to worship in their own way. They had already lived in New York, Ohio, Missouri, and Illinois. Now the Mormons, under the leadership of Brigham Young, traveled to the present-day land of Utah. In 1847, they came to the Great Salt Lake. They planted crops and raised cattle. They built a community that depended only on themselves. The settlement grew quickly.

When the war between the United States and Mexico ended, Utah and six other western states became part of the United States. One year later, in 1849, the Mormons asked that their land become a state. The government would not allow them to become a state, but they could be a territory. It was called the Utah Territory. Brigham Young became the governor.

Over the years, Brigham Young kept asking that Utah become a state. There were more Mormons than any other group in the territory. The government did not want one group to rule the area. They continued to say no. After some arguments, Brigham Young stepped down as governor.

You Can Visit Utah!

With the gold and silver mines booming in other western areas, people began to look in Utah, too. Some gold and silver was found, and mining companies began to grow. More people poured into the state. They needed land. The United States government began to move the Native Americans to reservations. Reservations were areas of land set aside for the Native Americans to live on. The people did not want to go. Some fighting broke out. Soon the Native Americans were forced to move.

Many new inventions were being made by the 1860s. Telegraph wires were hung from California to Washington. They were joined in Salt Lake City. Similarly, a railroad was built across the nation. It was joined in Promontory Point, Utah, in 1869. Utah was finally allowed to join the United States as a state in 1896.

The turn of the century brought huge growth to the state, both in people and factories. Irrigation was possible. The dry land of Utah could now be farmed.

New kinds of minerals, such as copper, lead, and coal, were found, and mining companies formed. The state was successful until the Great Depression. People were out of work. Utah was hit hard. The state began to recover during World War II. Mines began to open. Factories that built weapons and airplanes for the military opened in Utah. The factories continued working after the war, too. Uranium had been found. Uranium was used in atomic weapons.

More recently, Utah has looked to its future. As early as 1950, the state looked at environmental problems. People wanted Utah to be clean. They looked at ways to boost the water supply. Thanks to the government's farsightedness, Utah is a rugged but beautiful state today.

You Can Visit Utah!

Landscape

The Rocky Mountains, filled with basins, cut through the center of the state. In the southeast are deep canyons. Rivers ran through them. The winds and rain have further shaped the land into rock towers. Deserts cover almost one third of the state.

Climate

Like most western states, the climate of Utah varies. The mountains and plateau areas are cooler in the winter and summer. Overall, the state has an average temperature of 28° F in January and 77° F in July. Since there is little ground water, Utah depends on the rainfall and snow each year. The low areas receive less than 16 inches each year. The mountains receive from 16 to 40 inches on average.

Natural Resources

Utah has the largest number of minerals in the United States. They include copper, silver, gold, zinc, and uranium. Iron ore, coal, and gas are also found in the state. There are few trees, and the state has limited water supplies other than the few rivers and snow runoff.

Economy

The economy in Utah is very successful. The state manufactures airplane, missile, and rocket parts. Food processing and computer software are also important industries. The state nickname, the Beehive State, comes from its large production of honey. In mining, the state finds oil, copper, and uranium. However, the most important industry in Utah is service. People work in stores, banks, and real estate offices. They help tourists who visit the state. Many people also work for different branches of the government.

Higher Education

Utah is known for its educated population. Education has been important, from the time of the first Mormon settlement. In fact, the University of Deseret opened

You Can Visit Utah!

in 1850, three years after the Mormons settled in Salt Lake City. The school began in one room of an adobe cabin. The name was eventually changed to the University of Utah. Another college opened in 1875. It was named for Brigham Young, the Mormon leader. It was called Brigham Young University.

Famous People

Many interesting people have called Utah home. Butch Cassidy, an outlaw, hid in the canyons of Utah to escape being caught by law officers. Philo Farnsworth invented the television. Jim McMahon was a quarterback for the Chicago Bears football team. He helped the team win the 1985 Super Bowl Championship. The singers Donny and Marie Osmond are also from the state.

Utah Today

The state of Utah has seldom faced big problems. The state government has looked into the future to solve small problems before they have grown too big. Moreover, education has always

been important to the state. With an educated population come new ideas and new businesses. However, as more people move to Utah, the state may have some difficulties.

The lack of water has always been a concern in Utah. People need water to drink, cook with, and wash with. Businesses need it to produce the electricity that runs the factories. Right now, the government guesses there is enough water to last through the year 2020. Also, additional people mean more land will be used. Many people in Utah want the land to stay natural. They do not want it to be built on. But as their motto reads, "Industry," Utah will work to find a way to solve these problems as they move into the 21st century.

Assessment

Circle the letter of the correct answer.

1. The nickname of Utah is _____.
   a. the Mountain State
   b. the Mormon State
   c. the Beehive State
   d. the Waterless State

2. _____ was the leader of the Mormons.
   a. Donny Osmond
   b. Brigham Young
   c. Kit Carson
   d. Abraham Lincoln

3. For water, Utah depends on _____.
   a. its many rivers
   b. underground wells
   c. Civil War
   d. rain and snowfall

4. The most important industry in Utah is _____.
   a. food processing
   b. building airplanes
   c. teaching children
   d. service

5. Butch Cassidy _____ in the canyons of Utah.
   a. taught school
   b. hid from law officers
   c. sang to tourists
   d. played football

UTAH – The Beehive State

Travel Time!

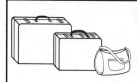

Pack Your Bags!

You will need:
- a road map
- resource books

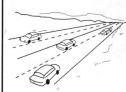

On the Road!

- Here is a list of places to visit in Utah. Research to find what each is famous for. Then find each place on a map.
  - Anasazi Indian Village State Park
  - Bonneville Salt Flats
  - Canyonlands National Park
  - Dinosaur National Monument
  - Earth Science Museum
  - Fremont Indian State Park
  - Golden Spike National Historic Site
  - Salt Lake City
  - Zion National Park

Snapshots

- Which place would you like to visit? Tell why.

_____

_____

_____

_____

_____

_____

UTAH – *The Beehive State*

State Your Facts!

Capital: Olympia

Abbreviation: WA

Statehood: November 11, 1889—
the 42nd state

Motto: *Alki* ("Bye and bye")

Bird: Willow goldfinch or wild canary

Flower: Coast rhododendron

Tree: Western hemlock

Area: 68,126 sq mi (176,446 sq km)—
20th in size

Five largest cities: Seattle, Spokane,
Tacoma, Bellevue, Everett

Highest point: Mount Rainier—14,410 ft
(4,392 m)

Sports teams: Seattle Mariners (baseball),
Seattle Seahawks (football), Seattle Supersonics (basketball)

Name _____ Date _____

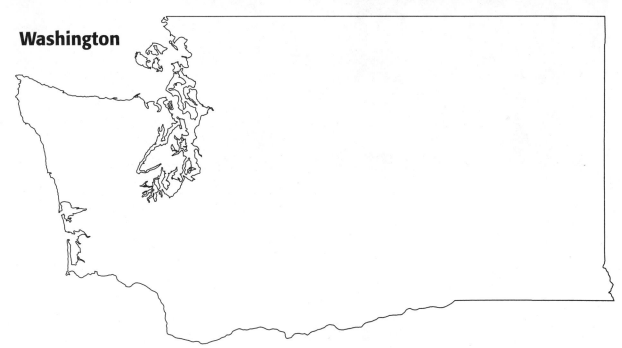

Washington

1. Find a map that shows the rivers of Washington. Then, on the map on this page, draw these rivers: Columbia, Yakima, Spokane, and Snake. Color the rivers blue.

2. Imagine that you could take a raft trip down one of these rivers. Which one would you choose? Write a story about your raft trip. Who would go with you? What problems would you have? How would you get around the dams on the rivers? Draw a picture of you and your raft.

3. Imagine that you noticed Mount St. Helens about to erupt. Other people did not believe you. What could you say to convince them to leave the area? Present your argument to the class. Include a picture of Mount St. Helens. What do you think it looked like while it was erupting?

4. Do research on famous volcanoes. They could be in North America or on other continents. Choose one and write a short essay about it. Share your information with the class. Include a picture of the volcano.

5. Many computer software companies are located in the Seattle area. What kind of software program would you like to make for a computer? What would the program do? Do you think it would be easy or hard to write a software program? Write a short essay about your ideas.

WASHINGTON – *The Evergreen State*

This Way to Washington!

Washington is the only state named after a U.S. President. The people of Washington work hard to make their state worthy of the name.

History

By 1775, about 70 different American Indian groups lived in the Washington area. Groups along the Pacific coast included the Chinook and Puyallup. They lived by fishing, trading, and gathering. Inland, other Indian groups included the Cayuse, Nez Percé, and Yakima. These people fished in rivers. They hunted elk, deer, and moose for food. They did not have permanent homes. They followed the migrating animals they hunted.

European explorers first arrived around 1550. Many more came in the late 1700s. Spanish explorer Bruno de Heceta arrived in 1775. British Captain James Cook explored the coast in 1778. Captain George Vancouver and his officer Peter Puget came in 1792. They mapped Puget Sound.

The first American explorer to visit the area was Robert Gray. He arrived in 1792. On his journey, Gray discovered the Columbia River. He named it after his ship. In 1804,

President Thomas Jefferson sent Meriwether Lewis and William Clark to the West. They were to find a land route to the Pacific Ocean. They arrived at the mouth of the Columbia River in 1805.

Fur traders moved into the area. It was a vast place called the Oregon Country. In 1843, the Oregon Trail opened. Settlers began to pour into the Oregon Country. The government wanted the Indian groups to leave. Many refused, and battles broke out. In 1858, though, the Indians were defeated. They were forced to move to reservations. By the late 1880s, over 300,000 settlers lived in the area. In 1889, Washington became the 42nd state.

Most people in Washington made a living by fishing, farming, or logging. In the 1930s, though, the Great Depression struck the state. Many people lost their jobs. To help people, the U.S. government began some big projects. The biggest was the Grand Coulee Dam, started in 1936. It is still the largest concrete dam in the U.S.

In May 1980, a very unusual thing happened in Washington. A volcano erupted. This does not happen much in the U.S. Mount St. Helens exploded on May 18.

WASHINGTON – The Evergreen State

This Way to Washington!

Everything within eight miles of the volcano was destroyed. All trees within 19 miles were knocked down. Over 50 people died, and many animals were killed, too.

Landscape

Washington is a medium-sized state. It measures about 239 miles (385 km) north to south. It is about 370 miles (595 km) wide. It has about 157 miles (253 km) of coastline on the Pacific Ocean.

In the northwest part is the Olympic Peninsula. It has a small amount of coastal plain. It also has one of the only rain forests in the U.S. The rest of the peninsula is covered by the rugged Olympic Mountains. Also in the northwest part of the state is Puget Sound. This long arm of the Pacific Ocean cuts deep into the west-central part of the state. Southwest Washington has coastal plains, hills, and low mountains. Here can be found many rivers, streams, and lakes. There are fertile valleys and forests, too.

The backbone of the state is the Cascade Mountain Range. These mountains are in west-central

Washington. They run from the Canada border to the Columbia River. There are also mountains in the northeast and southeast parts of the state. East of the Cascades is the Columbia Plateau. Some parts of the plateau have low hills and rolling land. Much of the plateau is a flat desert.

Climate

The climate of Washington varies from west to east. West of the Cascades, the state gets warming Pacific breezes. Here the climate is mild in winter and summer. East of the Cascades, the climate is more arid. The growing season in the state ranges from 80 to 260 days.

Rainfall in the state varies widely, too. The southwest slopes of the Olympic Mountains get about 142 inches of rain a year. The northeast edge of the Olympic Peninsula gets only about 17 inches a year. The Columbia Plateau gets 10 to 20 inches a year. Snowfall also varies widely. Some places in the Cascades get 400 inches of snow a year. Very little snow falls on the coastal area.

WASHINGTON – *The Evergreen State*

This Way to Washington!

Natural Resources

Washington has many natural resources. It has many sources of water. It gets fresh water from its many rivers and lakes. Two important rivers are the Columbia and the Snake. The state also gets hydroelectric power from fresh water. This power comes from the Grand Coulee Dam and other dams on the Columbia River. The  salt water of the Pacific Ocean provides seafood.

The many forests in the state provide timber for logging. Many materials are mined, too. These include coal, gravel, silver, and zinc.

Economy

One of the largest industries in the state is building airplanes. Computer software is important, too. Microsoft, the biggest software company in the world, is based in Redmond. Many other software companies are located in nearby Seattle.

Many people still work in logging, fishing, and farming. Washington is the number-one producer of apples in the U.S. Other people work in service jobs. Many service workers help tourists visiting the state.

Higher Education

Washington has a variety of fine colleges and universities. The University of Washington opened in 1861. Its main campus is in Seattle. Gonzaga University in Spokane was founded in 1887. It began as a frontier boarding school for boys.

Famous People

Many famous people have been from Washington. Bing Crosby was a famous singer and entertainer for many years. His most famous recording was "White Christmas." Minoru Yamasaki was a creative architect from Seattle. He designed the World Trade Center in New York City. As a founder of Microsoft, Bill Gates has become one of the richest people in the world.

Washington Today

In 1962 the Century 21 World's Fair was held in Seattle. People in Washington still look to the future. They work to preserve the beauty of their state.

WASHINGTON – The Evergreen State

Assessment

Circle the letter of the correct answer.

1. Washington is the only state named after a _____.
   a. mountain   **b.** President
   c. queen   **d.** river

2. The first American explorer to visit the Washington area was _____.
   a. James Cook
   b. James K. Polk
   c. Robert Gray
   d. George Washington

3. In 1980, a volcano named _____ erupted in Washington.
   a. Mount Olympus
   b. Mount Rainier
   c. Mount Cascade
   d. Mount St. Helens

4. Washington is the leading producer of _____ in the U.S.
   a. apples   **b.** volcanoes
   c. dams   **d.** music

Read each statement. Answer *true* or *false*.

_____ 5. The Cayuse and Nez Percé Indians lived in permanent villages.

_____ 6. President Jefferson sent Lewis and Clark to find a route to Mexico.

_____ 7. Washington became a state in 1789.

_____ 8. Grand Coulee Dam is made of concrete.

_____ 9. Some places in the Cascade Mountains get 400 inches of snow a year.

Travel Time!

There are many things to see and do in Washington. There are many sites related to American Indians. Many Indian groups hold powwows. The Tinowit International Powwow is held in Yakima each June. Drummers and dancers from all over the U.S. and Canada come to perform. Yakima is in south-central Washington. The Ellensburg Rodeo also features American Indian dances. It is held each Labor Day. Ellensburg is in central Washington, about 25 miles (40 km) north of Yakima. A festival honoring a famous chief is held in Suquamish. The Chief Seattle Days are held each August. Suquamish is in west-central Washington, near Seattle.

If you like music, go to Seattle. The Seattle Symphony Orchestra performs there. So does the Seattle Opera. Or you might like to see some rock music. The "grunge" sound started there in the early 1990s. Also visit the Space Needle. It was built in 1962 for the Century 21 World's Fair. Seattle is in west-central Washington, near Puget Sound.

If you enjoy nature, you will love Washington. The state has

three national parks. These are great for camping and hiking. In north-central Washington is North Cascades National Park. Olympic National Park is on the Olympic Peninsula. Mount Rainier National Park is in the west-central part of the state.

About 50 miles (80 km) southeast of Mount Rainier is another interesting site. This is the Mount St. Helens National Volcanic Monument. Here you can learn about the 1980 eruption and see how nature has recovered. There are also many national forests in the state. Many rivers and lakes offer other kinds of fun and adventure.

Another spectacular sight to see is Grand Coulee Dam. It is the largest concrete dam in the U.S. The dam is on the Columbia River, in east-central Washington. It is about 75 miles (120 km) west of Spokane.

WASHINGTON – *The Evergreen State*

Name _____ Date _____

Travel Time!

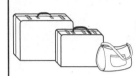

Pack Your Bags!

- Pretend your family is going on a one-week canoe trip down the Yakima River. You will start at its source in the Cascade Mountains. Find it on a map. Then you will head downstream toward Yakima and Kennewick. There are no hotels or restaurants along the way. What will you need to take on your one-week trip? Make a list. Will you need a tent and sleeping bags? Don't forget food and water. Plan a menu for each day's meals.

- How far do you think you can canoe in a week? Make an estimate. On the map, chart how far you will go each day. Where will you stop at the end of each day? What will you see along the way? Make a scrapbook about what this trip would be like.

On the Road!

- There are many fun things to do on a road trip. One fun thing is to find words on road signs and billboards. Try to find words that begin with each letter in your town's name. Try to find the words in the order of the letters in the name.

Snapshots

- Draw a picture of Grand Coulee Dam.
- Draw a picture of a totem pole. Include animal heads in your picture. Color the picture using bright colors.

State Your Facts!

Capital: Cheyenne

Abbreviation: WY

Statehood: July 10, 1890—
the 44th state

Motto: "Equal Rights"

Bird: Western meadowlark

Flower: Indian paintbrush

Tree: Cottonwood

Area: 97,914 sq mi (253,596 sq km)—
9th in size

Five largest cities: Casper, Cheyenne,
Rock Springs, Sheridan, Laramie

Highest point: Gannett Peak—
13,785 ft (4,208 m)

Name ______________________________ Date ____________________

Things To Do!

Map Index

Amethyst Mountain	B-4
Artist Point	C-3
Bechler Ranger Station	E-1
Eagle Peak	D-4
Fountain Paintpots	C-2
Lake Junction	C-3
Mammoth Hot Springs	A-2
Old Faithful Geyser	D-2
Overlook Mountain	E-3

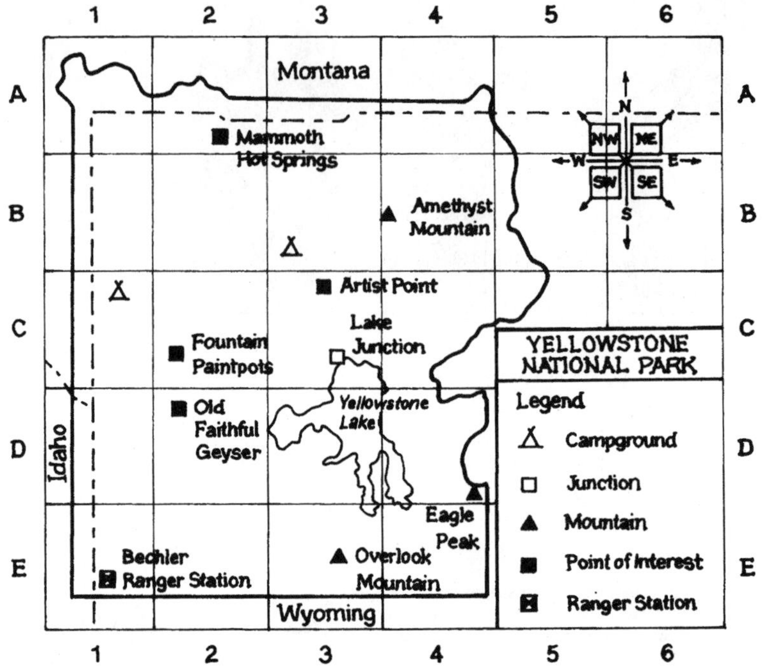

Look at the map of Yellowstone National Park in Wyoming. Then answer the questions.

1. Use the map index to find each place on the map. Draw a circle around each place.

Old Faithful Geyser	Mammoth Hot Springs
Lake Junction	Fountain Paintpots
Bechler Ranger Station	Amethyst Mountain

2. Find Artist Point on the map. Draw a circle around it. Write the direction you would travel from Artist Point to each place below. The first one is done for you.

a. Old Faithful Geyser ___*SW*___ **b.** Yellowstone Lake ________

c. Mammoth Hot Springs ________ **d.** Fountain Paintpots ________

e. Amethyst Mountain ________ **f.** Bechler Ranger Station ________

3. Find the symbol for a campground in the legend. Draw a campground symbol southwest of Mammoth Hot Springs.

4. The highest mountain peak in Yellowstone is in square D-4. What is the name of the mountain? ____________________

Winding Through Wyoming!

Wyoming has wide open plains. It also has mountains. Rivers flow through the state. Wyoming is the ninth largest state, but it has an average of five people per square mile. Alaska is the only state to have fewer people in the same area.

History

The present-day Wyoming was home to many Native Americans. Some followed the buffalo. Others trapped beaver. The Americans were the first people to explore this land. The Lewis and Clark team had traveled to California in 1806 to help find a trail between the east and west coast. John Colter, a member of the team, left the group to trap. He entered Wyoming. Native Americans caught him. After escaping, he traveled into the area now known as Yellowstone National Park. When he returned to the east coast, few people believed his tales of hot springs, water gushing from the Earth, and rocks that looked like trees.

Shortly, fur traders and trappers visited the area. The trappers and the Native Americans got along well. The trappers did no damage to the land. They only stayed in one place for a short time. A path through the Rocky Mountains was soon discovered. It was called the South Pass. People could pass through a valley without having to climb the tall mountains. The South Pass became an important part of history as pioneers made their way from the east coast to the west coast. The pass was part of the Oregon Trail. It wound its way across the plains and mountains of the land that would eventually be called *Wyoming*.

Pioneers gathered in Missouri. They brought only the things that could fit in a covered wagon. Many brought a few cattle. They would travel along the Oregon Trail through the South Pass. Some continued on to Oregon, California, or Utah. Some stayed in Wyoming. The first permanent settlement was built in 1834. The United States Army bought it. It was named Fort Laramie. The fort housed the United States Army.

WYOMING – The Equality State

Winding Through Wyoming!

Stagecoaches and telegraph lines began to cross the land. More and more people began farming in Wyoming. Native Americans became upset at the loss of their land. They began to attack the wagons, coaches, and settlers. In one attack, the Sioux killed 82 soldiers. The battle was known as the Fetterman Massacre. The United States began to force Native Americans to live on reservations. Reservations were small areas of land. Native Americans could live there in peace. However, it destroyed their way of life and took away their freedom.

In 1868, Wyoming became a territory. People began to move to the new territory. Many were cattle ranchers. They let the cows feed on the large, grassy prairies. Some were sheep ranchers. They lived in wagons and let the sheep feed on the grassy mountains. Others became farmers and fenced off their land. The women worked beside the men. Wyoming was the first place in the country to let women vote. It was also the first place to set aside land for a park. The people felt the area called Yellowstone had some wonderful parts of nature. They wanted to keep the land safe. Yellowstone was declared a park in 1872. The territory became a state in 1890.

Oil and coal were found in Wyoming at the turn of the century. The economy boomed. The state did not have too many problems during the Great Depression. The people in most states were out of work. But Wyoming kept mining coal and pumping oil out of wells. The state became even busier during World War II. The country needed meat, oil, coal, and lumber in the war. Again, in the 1970s, Wyoming was an important state. Oil, coal, and petroleum were in short supply. Wyoming had plenty. Workers rushed to the state. The state population began to grow.

Even with all the growth, the population of Wyoming is small. Some towns only have three people living in them. Much of the land still looks like it did when the Native Americans roamed on it. There are wide open plains and grass-covered mountains. Water and air pollution are not problems in this great state.

Winding Through Wyoming!

Landscape

There are three kinds of land in Wyoming. Over one third of the land is covered in mountains. Trees and grass cover the lower parts, while snow and rocks are at the higher regions. The basin is low and flat. Some parts are very dry. These areas are sandy, rocky areas. Another part of the state is known as the plains. The area is mostly flat and covered in grasses. It is not unusual to have a mesa rise up in the middle of the plains, though. A mesa is a mountain-like landform that is flat on the top. The state also has some interesting parts of nature that no other state in the nation has.

Climate

Wyoming does not get much rain. It is a very dry state. In the mountains, snow is the main source of precipitation. Some places receive up to 200 inches of snow. However, in the basins, snow averages only 12 inches.

Temperatures are cool, even in the summer. Average July temperatures are about 55° F. However, in the mountains, temperatures can drop to 32° F in the summer. Most winters are very cold. Temperatures range from 10° F to 25° F.

Natural Resources

The land is rich in Wyoming. There are large deposits of petroleum, coal, natural gas, and trona. Trona is a mineral used to make glass and paper. When mining these minerals, companies are very careful to protect the land. The beauty of the land is as much a resource as the minerals. Yellowstone National Park has many important parts of nature that no other place in the United States has. For example, Old Faithful is a geyser that shoots water into the air every 65 minutes.

Economy

The economy in Wyoming has been successful from the beginning. The state mines petroleum, natural gas, and coal. Mining is the state's main source of income.

WYOMING – *The Equality State*

Winding Through Wyoming!

Service is another important way Wyoming earns money. People work in transportation, communication, and utility. The government owns much of the land. So many people, like rangers, are hired to watch and take care of the land. Ranching of cattle and sheep is also important.

Higher Education

Wyoming has only one university. It is the University of Wyoming. It opened in 1887. It is known for its teaching of agriculture and engineering. The state does have other community colleges. Some are found in Casper, Sheridan, and Rock Springs.

Famous People

One of the well-known people from Wyoming is Chief Red Cloud. He was chief of the Sioux nation. He led his warriors against the settlers who invaded their land. Nellie Ross moved to Wyoming in 1902. Her husband became governor of the state in 1922. He died in 1924 while serving in office. The people of Wyoming voted for Nellie to take his place. She was

the first woman governor in the United States. Jackson Pollock is also from Wyoming. He is a painter who uses bright colors and shapes in his art.

Wyoming Today

Wyoming has few people and few manufacturing plants. It has been good for the state. There are no problems with air or water pollution. There is no overcrowding. The land has always taken care of the people living there. The people want to protect the special beauty of the land. After all, they were the first state to make land into a state park to keep it safe. Just like other western states, the only problem they might face is the lack of water. But Wyoming will look ahead. The people always take care of their land.

Assessment

Circle the letter of the correct answer.

1. Wyoming has an average of _____ people living in a square mile.
   - **a.** five
   - **b.** fifty
   - **c.** five hundred
   - **d.** five thousand

2. _____ was the first American to see Wyoming.
   - **a.** Jackson Pollock
   - **b.** Brigham Young
   - **c.** John Colter
   - **d.** William Fetterman

3. The _____ was a way to get through the Rocky Mountains.
   - **a.** Oregon Trail
   - **b.** South Pass
   - **c.** Fort Laramie
   - **d.** First Pass

4. Wyoming was the first state that let women _____.
   - **a.** own ranches and cattle
   - **b.** teach children
   - **c.** fight in the army
   - **d.** vote in elections

5. _____ was the first land to be made into a park.
   - **a.** Yellowstone
   - **b.** Rocky Mountains
   - **c.** Grand Tetons
   - **d.** Black Canyon

6. The government owns much _____ in Wyoming.
   - **a.** cattle
   - **b.** coal
   - **c.** money
   - **d.** land

WYOMING – *The Equality State*

Name _____ Date _____

Travel Time!

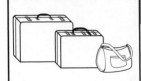

Pack Your Bags!

You will need:
- a United States Map
- resource books

On the Road!

- Beginning around 1830, many people left the east coast. They traveled west in search of land and gold. These pioneers followed the Oregon Trail. The Oregon Trail began in Independence, Missouri. It was 2,000 miles long. Some people decided to settle in Wyoming to set up ranches.

- Suppose you are a pioneer getting ready to begin a trip to Wyoming. Your family will start a ranch in Wyoming. You will be traveling in a wagon on the Oregon Trail. Research about the Oregon Trail. Plan for your trip. The questions below will help you.
  - How long will the trip take?
  - What kind of food and how much of it will you need to take?
  - What kinds of things will you need to take to start a ranch?
  - Your parents say you can take one special item. What would it be? Why?

Snapshots

- Draw a picture of yourself in a wagon. Write a paragraph about what it would be like to ride on the Oregon Trail in the 1830s.